TEACHER'S GUIDE

Connected ⊛ Mathematics 2™

Variables and Patterns

Introducing Algebra

$c = 21n$

1.1
1.2
1.3
1.4
1.5
✓ up
2.1
2.2
2.3
3.1
3.2 1.5 days
3.3 1.5 days
Review & Test 2 days

Glenda Lappan
James T. Fey
William M. Fitzgerald
Susan N. Friel
Elizabeth Difanis Phillips

PEARSON

Boston, Massachusetts · Glenview, Illinois · Shoreview, Minnesota · Upper Saddle River, New Jersey

Connected Mathematics™ was developed at Michigan State University with financial support from the Michigan State University Office of the Provost, Computing and Technology, and the College of Natural Science.

This material is based upon work supported by the National Science Foundation under Grant No. MDR 9150217 and Grant No. ESI 9986372. Opinions expressed are those of the authors and not necessarily those of the Foundation.

The Michigan State University authors and administration have agreed that all MSU royalties arising from this publication will be devoted to purposes supported by the Department of Mathematics and the MSU Mathematics Enrichment Fund.

13-digit ISBN 978-0-13-366192-7
10-digit ISBN 0-13-366192-X
2 3 4 5 6 7 8 9 10   11 10 09 08

Authors of Connected Mathematics

(from left to right) Glenda Lappan, Betty Phillips, Susan Friel, Bill Fitzgerald, Jim Fey

Glenda Lappan is a University Distinguished Professor in the Department of Mathematics at Michigan State University. Her research and development interests are in the connected areas of students' learning of mathematics and mathematics teachers' professional growth and change related to the development and enactment of K–12 curriculum materials.

James T. Fey is a Professor of Curriculum and Instruction and Mathematics at the University of Maryland. His consistent professional interest has been development and research focused on curriculum materials that engage middle and high school students in problem-based collaborative investigations of mathematical ideas and their applications.

William M. Fitzgerald (*Deceased*) was a Professor in the Department of Mathematics at Michigan State University. His early research was on the use of concrete materials in supporting student learning and led to the development of teaching materials for laboratory environments. Later he helped develop a teaching model to support student experimentation with mathematics.

Susan N. Friel is a Professor of Mathematics Education in the School of Education at the University of North Carolina at Chapel Hill. Her research interests focus on statistics education for middle-grade students and, more broadly, on teachers' professional development and growth in teaching mathematics K–8.

Elizabeth Difanis Phillips is a Senior Academic Specialist in the Mathematics Department of Michigan State University. She is interested in teaching and learning mathematics for both teachers and students. These interests have led to curriculum and professional development projects at the middle school and high school levels, as well as projects related to the teaching and learning of algebra across the grades.

CMP2 Development Staff

Teacher Collaborator in Residence
Yvonne Grant
Michigan State University

Production and Field Site Manager
Lisa Keller
Michigan State University

Administrative Assistant
Judith Martus Miller
Michigan State University

Technical and Editorial Support
Brin Keller, Peter Lappan, Jim Laser,
Michael Masterson, Stacey Miceli

Assessment Team
June Bailey and Debra Sobko (Apollo Middle School, Rochester, New York), George Bright (University of North Carolina, Greensboro), Gwen Ranzau Campbell (Sunrise Park Middle School, White Bear Lake, Minnesota), Holly DeRosia, Kathy Dole, and Teri Keusch (Portland Middle School, Portland, Michigan), Mary Beth Schmitt (Traverse City East Junior High School, Traverse City, Michigan), Genni Steele (Central Middle School, White Bear Lake, Minnesota), Jacqueline Stewart (Okemos, Michigan), Elizabeth Tye (Magnolia Junior High School, Magnolia, Arkansas)

Development Assistants
At Lansing Community College *Undergraduate Assistant:* James Brinegar

At Michigan State University *Graduate Assistants:* Dawn Berk, Emily Bouck, Bulent Buyukbozkirli, Kuo-Liang Chang, Christopher Danielson, Srinivasa Dharmavaram, Deb Johanning, Wesley Kretzschmar, Kelly Rivette, Sarah Sword, Tat Ming Sze, Marie Turini, Jeffrey Wanko; *Undergraduate Assistants:* Daniel Briggs, Jeffrey Chapin, Jade Corsé, Elisha Hardy, Alisha Harold, Elizabeth Keusch, Julia Letoutchaia, Karen Loeffler, Brian Oliver, Carl Oliver, Evonne Pedawi, Lauren Rebrovich

At the University of Maryland *Graduate Assistants:* Kim Harris Bethea, Kara Karch

At the University of North Carolina (Chapel Hill) *Graduate Assistants:* Mark Ellis, Trista Stearns; *Undergraduate Assistant:* Daniel Smith

Advisory Board for CMP2

Thomas Banchoff
Professor of Mathematics
Brown University
Providence, Rhode Island

Anne Bartel
Mathematics Coordinator
Minneapolis Public Schools
Minneapolis, Minnesota

Hyman Bass
Professor of Mathematics
University of Michigan
Ann Arbor, Michigan

Joan Ferrini-Mundy
Associate Dean of the College of
Natural Science; Professor
Michigan State University
East Lansing, Michigan

James Hiebert
Professor
University of Delaware
Newark, Delaware

Susan Hudson Hull
Charles A. Dana Center
University of Texas
Austin, Texas

Michele Luke
Mathematics Curriculum
Coordinator
West Junior High
Minnetonka, Minnesota

Kay McClain
Assistant Professor of
Mathematics Education
Vanderbilt University
Nashville, Tennessee

Edward Silver
Professor; Chair of Educational
Studies
University of Michigan
Ann Arbor, Michigan

Judith Sowder
Professor Emerita
San Diego State University
San Diego, California

Lisa Usher
Mathematics Resource Teacher
California Academy of
Mathematics and Science
San Pedro, California

Field Test Sites for CMP2

During the development of the revised edition of *Connected Mathematics* (CMP2), more than 100 classroom teachers have field-tested materials at 49 school sites in 12 states and the District of Columbia. This classroom testing occurred over three academic years (2001 through 2004), allowing careful study of the effectiveness of each of the 24 units that comprise the program. A special thanks to the students and teachers at these pilot schools.

Arkansas
Magnolia Public Schools
Kittena Bell*, Judith Trowell*; *Central Elementary School:* Maxine Broom, Betty Eddy, Tiffany Fallin, Bonnie Flurry, Carolyn Monk, Elizabeth Tye; *Magnolia Junior High School:* Monique Bryan, Ginger Cook, David Graham, Shelby Lamkin

Colorado
Boulder Public Schools
Nevin Platt Middle School: Judith Koenig

St. Vrain Valley School District, Longmont
Westview Middle School: Colleen Beyer, Kitty Canupp, Ellie Decker*, Peggy McCarthy, Tanya deNobrega, Cindy Payne, Ericka Pilon, Andrew Roberts

District of Columbia
Capitol Hill Day School: Ann Lawrence

Georgia
University of Georgia, Athens
Brad Findell

Madison Public Schools
Morgan County Middle School: Renee Burgdorf, Lynn Harris, Nancy Kurtz, Carolyn Stewart

Maine
Falmouth Public Schools
Falmouth Middle School: Donna Erikson, Joyce Hebert, Paula Hodgkins, Rick Hogan, David Legere, Cynthia Martin, Barbara Stiles, Shawn Towle*

Michigan
Portland Public Schools
Portland Middle School: Mark Braun, Holly DeRosia, Kathy Dole*, Angie Foote, Teri Keusch, Tammi Wardwell

Traverse City Area Public Schools
Bertha Vos Elementary: Kristin Sak; *Central Grade School:* Michelle Clark; Jody Meyers; *Eastern Elementary:* Karrie Tufts; *Interlochen Elementary:* Mary McGee-Cullen; *Long Lake Elementary:* Julie Faulkner*, Charlie Maxbauer, Katherine Sleder; *Norris Elementary:* Hope Slanaker; *Oak Park Elementary:* Jessica Steed; *Traverse Heights Elementary:* Jennifer Wolfert; *Westwoods Elementary:* Nancy Conn; *Old Mission Peninsula School:* Deb Larimer; *Traverse City East Junior High:* Ivanka Berkshire, Ruthanne Kladder, Jan Palkowski, Jane Peterson, Mary Beth Schmitt; *Traverse City West Junior High:* Dan Fouch*, Ray Fouch

Sturgis Public Schools
Sturgis Middle School: Ellen Eisele

Minnesota
Burnsville School District 191
Hidden Valley Elementary: Stephanie Cin, Jane McDevitt

Hopkins School District 270
Alice Smith Elementary: Sandra Cowing, Kathleen Gustafson, Martha Mason, Scott Stillman; *Eisenhower Elementary:* Chad Bellig, Patrick Berger, Nancy Glades, Kye Johnson, Shane Wasserman, Victoria Wilson; *Gatewood Elementary:* Sarah Ham, Julie Kloos, Janine Pung, Larry Wade; *Glen Lake Elementary:* Jacqueline Cramer, Kathy Hering, Cecelia Morris,

Robb Trenda; *Katherine Curren Elementary:* Diane Bancroft, Sue DeWit, John Wilson; *L. H. Tanglen Elementary:* Kevin Athmann, Lisa Becker, Mary LaBelle, Kathy Rezac, Roberta Severson; *Meadowbrook Elementary:* Jan Gauger, Hildy Shank, Jessica Zimmerman; *North Junior High:* Laurel Hahn, Kristin Lee, Jodi Markuson, Bruce Mestemacher, Laurel Miller, Bonnie Rinker, Jeannine Salzer, Sarah Shafer, Cam Stottler; *West Junior High:* Alicia Beebe, Kristie Earl, Nobu Fujii, Pam Georgetti, Susan Gilbert, Regina Nelson Johnson, Debra Lindstrom, Michele Luke*, Jon Sorensen

Minneapolis School District 1
Ann Sullivan K–8 School: Bronwyn Collins; Anne Bartel* (Curriculum and Instruction Office)

Wayzata School District 284
Central Middle School: Sarajane Myers, Dan Nielsen, Tanya Ravnholdt

White Bear Lake School District 624
Central Middle School: Amy Jorgenson, Michelle Reich, Brenda Sammon

New York
New York City Public Schools
IS 89: Yelena Aynbinder, Chi-Man Ng, Nina Rapaport, Joel Spengler, Phyllis Tam*, Brent Wyso; *Wagner Middle School:* Jason Appel, Intissar Fernandez, Yee Gee Get, Richard Goldstein, Irving Marcus, Sue Norton, Bernadita Owens, Jennifer Rehn*, Kevin Yuhas

---

* indicates a Field Test Site Coordinator

Ohio
Talawanda School District, Oxford
Talawanda Middle School: Teresa Abrams, Larry Brock, Heather Brosey, Julie Churchman, Monna Even, Karen Fitch, Bob George, Amanda Klee, Pat Meade, Sandy Montgomery, Barbara Sherman, Lauren Steidl
Miami University
Jeffrey Wanko*
Springfield Public Schools
Rockway School: Jim Mamer

Pennsylvania
Pittsburgh Public Schools
Kenneth Labuskes, Marianne O'Connor, Mary Lynn Raith*; *Arthur J. Rooney Middle School:* David Hairston, Stamatina Mousetis, Alfredo Zangaro; *Frick International Studies Academy:* Suzanne Berry, Janet Falkowski, Constance Finseth, Romika Hodge, Frank Machi; *Reizenstein Middle School:* Jeff Baldwin, James Brautigam, Lorena Burnett, Glen Cobbett, Michael Jordan, Margaret Lazur, Tamar McPherson, Melissa Munnell, Holly Neely, Ingrid Reed, Dennis Reft

Texas
Austin Independent School District
Bedichek Middle School: Lisa Brown, Jennifer Glasscock, Vicki Massey
El Paso Independent School District
Cordova Middle School: Armando Aguirre, Anneliesa Durkes, Sylvia Guzman, Pat Holguin*, William Holguin, Nancy Nava, Laura Orozco, Michelle Peña, Roberta Rosen, Patsy Smith, Jeremy Wolf
Plano Independent School District
Patt Henry, James Wohlgehagen*; *Frankford Middle School:* Mandy Baker, Cheryl Butsch, Amy Dudley, Betsy Eshelman, Janet Greene, Cort Haynes, Kathy Letchworth, Kay Marshall, Kelly McCants, Amy Reck, Judy Scott, Syndy Snyder, Lisa Wang; *Wilson Middle School:* Darcie Bane, Amanda Bedenko, Whitney Evans, Tonelli Hatley, Sarah (Becky) Higgs, Kelly Johnston, Rebecca McElligott, Kay Neuse, Cheri Slocum, Kelli Straight

Washington
Evergreen School District
Shahala Middle School: Nicole Abrahamsen, Terry Coon*, Carey Doyle, Sheryl Drechsler, George Gemma, Gina Helland, Amy Hilario, Darla Lidyard, Sean McCarthy, Tilly Meyer, Willow Nuewelt, Todd Parsons, Brian Pederson, Stan Posey, Shawn Scott, Craig Sjoberg, Lynette Sundstrom, Charles Switzer, Luke Youngblood

Wisconsin
Beaver Dam Unified School District
Beaver Dam Middle School: Jim Braemer, Jeanne Frick, Jessica Greatens, Barbara Link, Dennis McCormick, Karen Michels, Nancy Nichols*, Nancy Palm, Shelly Stelsel, Susan Wiggins

---

* indicates a Field Test Site Coordinator

Reviews of CMP to Guide Development of CMP2

Before writing for CMP2 began or field tests were conducted, the first edition of *Connected Mathematics* was submitted to the mathematics faculties of school districts from many parts of the country and to 80 individual reviewers for extensive comments.

School District Survey Reviews of CMP

Arizona
Madison School District #38 (Phoenix)

Arkansas
Cabot School District, Little Rock School District, Magnolia School District

California
Los Angeles Unified School District

Colorado
St. Vrain Valley School District (Longmont)

Florida
Leon County Schools (Tallahassee)

Illinois
School District #21 (Wheeling)

Indiana
Joseph L. Block Junior High (East Chicago)

Kentucky
Fayette County Public Schools (Lexington)

Maine
Selection of Schools

Massachusetts
Selection of Schools

Michigan
Sparta Area Schools

Minnesota
Hopkins School District

Texas
Austin Independent School District, The El Paso Collaborative for Academic Excellence, Plano Independent School District

Wisconsin
Platteville Middle School

Individual Reviewers of CMP

Arkansas
Deborah Cramer; Robby Frizzell *(Taylor)*; Lowell Lynde *(University of Arkansas, Monticello)*; Leigh Manzer *(Norfork)*; Lynne Roberts *(Emerson High School, Emerson)*; Tony Timms *(Cabot Public Schools)*; Judith Trowell *(Arkansas Department of Higher Education)*

California
José Alcantar *(Gilroy)*; Eugenie Belcher *(Gilroy)*; Marian Pasternack *(Lowman M. S. T. Center, North Hollywood)*; Susana Pezoa *(San Jose)*; Todd Rabusin *(Hollister)*; Margaret Siegfried *(Ocala Middle School, San Jose)*; Polly Underwood *(Ocala Middle School, San Jose)*

Colorado
Janeane Golliher *(St. Vrain Valley School District, Longmont)*; Judith Koenig *(Nevin Platt Middle School, Boulder)*

Florida
Paige Loggins *(Swift Creek Middle School, Tallahassee)*

Illinois
Jan Robinson *(School District #21, Wheeling)*

Indiana
Frances Jackson *(Joseph L. Block Junior High, East Chicago)*

Kentucky
Natalee Feese *(Fayette County Public Schools, Lexington)*

Maine
Betsy Berry *(Maine Math & Science Alliance, Augusta)*

Maryland
Joseph Gagnon *(University of Maryland, College Park)*; Paula Maccini *(University of Maryland, College Park)*

Massachusetts
George Cobb *(Mt. Holyoke College, South Hadley)*; Cliff Kanold *(University of Massachusetts, Amherst)*

Michigan
Mary Bouck *(Farwell Area Schools)*; Carol Dorer *(Slauson Middle School, Ann Arbor)*; Carrie Heaney *(Forsythe Middle School, Ann Arbor)*; Ellen Hopkins *(Clague Middle School, Ann Arbor)*; Teri Keusch *(Portland Middle School, Portland)*; Valerie Mills *(Oakland Schools, Waterford)*; Mary Beth Schmitt *(Traverse City East Junior High, Traverse City)*; Jack Smith *(Michigan State University, East Lansing)*; Rebecca Spencer *(Sparta Middle School, Sparta)*; Ann Marie Nicoll Turner *(Tappan Middle School, Ann Arbor)*; Scott Turner *(Scarlett Middle School, Ann Arbor)*

Minnesota
Margarita Alvarez *(Olson Middle School, Minneapolis)*; Jane Amundson *(Nicollet Junior High, Burnsville)*; Anne Bartel *(Minneapolis Public Schools)*; Gwen Ranzau Campbell *(Sunrise Park Middle School, White Bear Lake)*; Stephanie Cin *(Hidden Valley Elementary, Burnsville)*; Joan Garfield *(University of Minnesota, Minneapolis)*; Gretchen Hall *(Richfield Middle School, Richfield)*; Jennifer Larson *(Olson Middle School, Minneapolis)*; Michele Luke *(West Junior High, Minnetonka)*; Jeni Meyer *(Richfield Junior High, Richfield)*; Judy Pfingsten *(Inver Grove Heights Middle School, Inver Grove Heights)*; Sarah Shafer *(North Junior High, Minnetonka)*; Genni Steele *(Central Middle School, White Bear Lake)*; Victoria Wilson *(Eisenhower Elementary, Hopkins)*; Paul Zorn *(St. Olaf College, Northfield)*

New York
Debra Altenau-Bartolino *(Greenwich Village Middle School, New York)*; Doug Clements *(University of Buffalo)*; Francis Curcio *(New York University, New York)*; Christine Dorosh *(Clinton School for Writers, Brooklyn)*; Jennifer Rehn *(East Side Middle School, New York)*; Phyllis Tam *(IS 89 Lab School, New York)*; Marie Turini *(Louis Armstrong Middle School, New York)*; Lucy West *(Community School District 2, New York)*; Monica Witt *(Simon Baruch Intermediate School 104, New York)*

Pennsylvania
Robert Aglietti *(Pittsburgh)*; Sharon Mihalich *(Freeport)*; Jennifer Plumb *(South Hills Middle School, Pittsburgh)*; Mary Lynn Raith *(Pittsburgh Public Schools)*

Texas
Michelle Bittick *(Austin Independent School District)*; Margaret Cregg *(Plano Independent School District)*; Sheila Cunningham *(Klein Independent School District)*; Judy Hill *(Austin Independent School District)*; Patricia Holguin *(El Paso Independent School District)*; Bonnie McNemar *(Arlington)*; Kay Neuse *(Plano Independent School District)*; Joyce Polanco *(Austin Independent School District)*; Marge Ramirez *(University of Texas at El Paso)*; Pat Rossman *(Baker Campus, Austin)*; Cindy Schimek *(Houston)*; Cynthia Schneider *(Charles A. Dana Center, University of Texas at Austin)*; Uri Treisman *(Charles A. Dana Center, University of Texas at Austin)*; Jacqueline Weilmuenster *(Grapevine-Colleyville Independent School District)*; LuAnn Weynand *(San Antonio)*; Carmen Whitman *(Austin Independent School District)*; James Wohlgehagen *(Plano Independent School District)*

Washington
Ramesh Gangolli *(University of Washington, Seattle)*

Wisconsin
Susan Lamon *(Marquette University, Hales Corner)*; Steve Reinhart *(retired, Chippewa Falls Middle School, Eau Claire)*

Variables and Patterns
Introducing Algebra

The Student Edition pages for the Unit Opener follow page 14.

Variables and Patterns
Introducing Algebra

Goals of the Unit

- Identify quantitative variables in situations

- Recognize situations where changes in variables are related in useful patterns

- Describe patterns of change shown in words, tables, and graphs of data

- Construct tables and graphs to display relations among variables

- Observe relationships between two quantitative variables as shown in a table, graph, or equation and describe how the relationship can be seen in each of the other forms of representation

- Use algebraic symbols to write rules and equations relating variables

- Use tables, graphs, and equations to solve problems

- Use graphing calculators to construct tables and graphs of relations between variables and to answer questions about these relations

Developing Students' Mathematical Habits

The overall goal of the *Connected Mathematics* curriculum is to help students develop sound mathematical habits. Through their work in this and other algebra units, students learn important questions to ask themselves about situations that can be modeled mathematically.

- *What are the variables in the problem?*

- *How are these variables related to each other?*

- *Which variables depend on, or change in relation to, others?*

- *How can the relationship be displayed and analyzed with tables, graphs and equations?*

- *What does it mean when we see regular and predictable changes in a table of data or a graph?*

- *How can we use these predictable changes to solve problems?*

Overview

Situations that change are a part of everyone's life. Some situations change in predictable patterns. Others change in ways that seem beyond our ability to anticipate. It is human nature to want to analyze, anticipate, and predict how things change. Learning to observe, describe, and record changes is the first step in analyzing and searching for patterns in a real-world situation.

The central theme of the *Connected Mathematics* approach to algebra is the importance of studying relationships among quantitative variables. Those relationships are commonly represented in mathematics by tables of (x, y) data pairs, by graphs of related data values, by statements that describe (in words) the way the variables are related, and by equations that describe the relationship between x and y in compact symbolic form.

Variables and Patterns, the first unit of the *Connected Mathematics* algebra strand, develops students' ability to explore a variety of situations in which changes occur. In the first part of the unit, students explore three ways of representing a changing situation: in the narrative, with a data table, and with a graph. These three methods of organizing and recording data are revisited throughout the unit. They are compared to one another to elicit the strengths of each presentation.

In practice, effective use of both tables and graphs requires mathematical judgments. In the case of tables, one has to decide which values of the independent variable should be represented in the table to give most informative results. Should the value of the independent variable be shown in increments of 1, 2, 5, or 10? How far should the table extend?

In the case of graphs, one has to identify the independent and dependent variables in the relationship being studied, make choices of appropriate scales on the horizontal and vertical axes, plot a sample of (x, y) data points, and make decisions about whether and how those data points should be connected.

Effective use of graphs also requires the ability to "read" the numerical story from the shape of a function graph. For graphs that represent change over time, interpretation requires understanding that as one moves along the graph from left to right, a rising graph means an increasing value of the dependent variable, while a falling graph means a decreasing value of the dependent variable.

Later in the unit, students begin to write symbolic equations as a shorter, quicker way to give a summary of the relationship between two variables. This work comes only after extensive time and effort are devoted to analyzing data sets showing change and describing the change in words. The advantages of an equation over a data table or graph are investigated. Students do not learn systematic strategies to solve equations in this unit. However, they do use informal reasoning to find values for x or y given a value for the other. After becoming comfortable in writing equations, students learn how to use graphing calculators to make tables and graphs for any given equation.

The organization of this unit reflects the growing body of experience in function-oriented approaches to algebra, which suggests that students are more comfortable studying quantitative relationships if they work first from numerical data, usually displayed in tabular form. The unit interweaves graphs, tables, verbal descriptions, and equations to support students who are more comfortable with particular forms of representation. However, the goal is for all students to make progress in understanding and being able to think and reason with all major useful forms of representation.

Summary of Investigations

Investigation 1

Variables, Tables, and Coordinate Graphs

Investigation 1 introduces the idea of a variable and three different ways to represent relationships between variables: verbal descriptions, tables, and graphs. The context for the problems is the planning of a bike tour by a group of college students. Students interpret and create data representations and begin to think about the strengths and weaknesses of each type of representation.

Investigation 2
Analyzing Graphs and Tables

Investigation 2 focuses on making and using tables and graphs to help make decisions about costs and profit for the bike tour. The last problem involves matching verbal descriptions with related graphs.

Investigation 3
Rules and Equations

Investigation 3 develops strategies for writing symbolic equations, or formulas, to represent relationships between quantitative variables. Students first write equations involving one operation, and then move to two-operation equations. The last problem involves writing equations for revenue, expenses, and profit for the bike tour.

Investigation 4
Calculator Tables and Graphs

Investigation 4 has two problems that help students learn to make and use tables and graphs on a graphing calculator. The last problem allows students to review the strategies and techniques developed in Investigations 1–3 and compares their own work with tables and graphs generated on a graphing calculator.

Mathematics Background

Algebra

Through their work in this unit, your students learn that a variable is a quantity that might assume many different values. Students work on problems that require them to predict the pattern of change in a variable as time passes or to predict the way changes in values of one variable are related to changes in values of another. This unit introduces some basic tools of algebra. Students are not expected to develop a complete understanding of algebraic ideas. These ideas will be revisited and further developed in each of the succeeding algebra units.

Verbal Descriptions

Verbal descriptions of a relationship are useful because they are descriptions in students' everyday language. This helps students form mental pictures of the situations and the relationships among the variables. The disadvantage of verbal descriptions is that they are sometimes ambiguous, making it difficult to get a quick overview of the situation and the relationships among variables.

Tables

Tables are usually easy to read. From a table, you can see how a change in one variable affects the value of the other variable. Students can recognize whether the change is additive, multiplicative, or unpredictable. Once students recognize the pattern of change, they can extend the pattern to get the next entry. For example, consider these tables.

Table 1: Linear Relationship			
x	0	1	2	3
y	5	6	7	8

Table 1: Exponential Relationship			
x	0	1	2	3
y	1	2	4	8

In Table 1, as the values of the variable x change by 1 unit, the values of y change by 1 unit. Adding 1 to the previous entry in the x column and 1 to the previous entry in the y column can continue the table. If x is 3, then y is $7 + 1$, or 8. The particular change pattern in Table 1 is indicative of all *linear relationships*.

The change pattern in Table 2 is characteristic of *exponential relationships*. It is a multiplicative pattern because the values of y double, or increase by a factor of 2, as the values of x increase by 1 unit.

In some tables, the patterns of change are not regular. For example, Table 3, which occurs in the first investigation, does not show a pattern of change that is regular; that is, there is no way to predict the change from one point to the next.

**Table 3:
Unpredictable Change**

Time (hr)	Distance (mi)
0.0	0
0.5	8
1.0	15
1.5	19
2.0	25
2.5	27
3.0	34
3.5	40
4.0	40
4.5	40
5.0	45

Graphs

Graphs are another way to view relationships and patterns of change between variables. Graphs 1 and 2 can be thought of as pictures of the relationships in Tables 1 and 2.

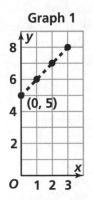
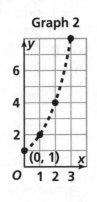

The linear relationship, which has a constant rate of change, is represented by a straight-line graph. The exponential relationship, which has a multiplicative rate of change, is characterized by a curve. These relationships can be represented symbolically as $y = x + 5$ (Table 1 and Graph 1) and $y = 2^x$ (Table 2 and Graph 2). Both of these patterns are explored in future units. Linear relationships are the focus of *Moving Straight Ahead*, and exponential relationship is studied in the grade 8 unit *Growing, Growing, Growing*.

This unit provides a foundation to study important patterns of change. Only simple linear

equations are explored in this unit. For example, the distance, d, a cyclist can cover depends on time, t, and the rate, r, at which the cyclist pedals. If a cyclist rides at a steady rate of 10 miles per hour, then $d = 10t$. This is a linear relation. Its graph is a straight line.

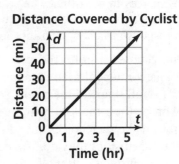

The shape of a graph of a pattern of change over time shows the rate of change in the dependent variable as time passes. A straight-line graph indicates change at a constant rate. A curved graph indicates change at a variable rate. For graphs that represent correlated change between two variables, in which the independent variable is *not* time, the interpretation is similar, except that instead of representing time, the independent variable is some other *manipulated variable* that produces correlated change in a *responding variable*, such as the profit changing as the number of books sold increases.

Graphs are more abstract than tables for many students. Therefore, the problems in the unit address with some care the issues that arise in constructing graphs of relationships between variables and the interpretation of the resulting "pictures." The problems provide specific guidance on the basic steps required in graph construction, and sort out issues about ways it might make sense to connect the known data points. Students go through the steps of graph construction and interpretation, using given data as well as data they collect from a jumping jack experiment.

Construction and analysis of graphs of quantitative relationships are tasks that students will meet again and again as they move through high school and college mathematics. This unit begins building the understanding and skill required by those tasks. It seems important to focus on two key ideas about graphs:

• Each point on a graph represents an ordered pair of values. The first number, or *coordinate*, in the ordered pair is a specific value of the independent variable. The second number is the corresponding value of the dependent variable. For example, time is the independent variable and distance is the dependent variable in the preceding example.

- The collection of points on a graph tells a "story" of how changes in one variable are related to changes in the other. The story might be one of change over time or of one variable's change in response to change in another.

As students choose scales for the axes of a graph, plot data points, connect plotted data points, and interpret the overall shape of the graph, you should consistently probe their thinking with questions about why they make the choices they do and how they draw the conclusions they do. To keep the issues in mind, plan on asking the following questions throughout the unit:

- *What is the shape of the graph?*
- *What choices did you make to construct the graph?*
- *How do you know you are right?*

Discrete versus Continuous Data

From a statistical perspective, there are two basic families of quantitative variables—those that can take on only a countable set of values (discrete data) and those that can take on essentially any real-number value in an interval (continuous data). When constructing tables or graphs of relationships between variables there is some value in recognizing whether one or both of the variables involved are discrete or continuous. Tables can represent only discrete collections of (x, y) values; graphs can better represent continuous variables. In fact, it is not uncommon to use a continuous graph to represent relationships in which one or both of the variables are limited to a discrete domain or range. Such continuous graphs help suggest the pattern of the relationship and, when the variables are discrete but with fairly dense possible values, the continuous graph is not usually misleading.

In this first algebra unit of *Connected Mathematics*, we pay some attention to questions about whether variables are discrete or continuous, mostly in the spirit of getting students to ask themselves questions such as:

- *What values make sense for the variables I'm studying?*
- *Does it make sense to connect the points on the graph?*

- *Does it make sense to try to find values between those on the graph?*

Many situations are discrete relationships, such as the number of sweatshirts sold and the revenue. If the shirts sell for $5.50, then the revenue, r, for selling n shirts is $r = 5.50n$. In this situation, it does not make sense to connect the points. Points $(1, 5.50)$ and $(2, 11)$ are on the graph; however, if these two points are connected it would imply that $1\frac{1}{2}$ or part of a shirt could be sold.

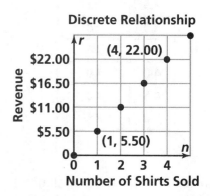

Discrete Relationship

Other situations, such as the distance/time/rate relation, are not discrete; they are continuous. For example, if a bicyclist pedals at a steady rate of 10 miles per hour, then distance, d, after t hours is $d = 10t$. In the graph of $d = 10t$, it is reasonable to connect the points $(1, 10)$ and $(2, 20)$ since one can travel $1\frac{1}{2}$ hours and go a distance of 15 miles; it makes sense because time is a continuous quantity.

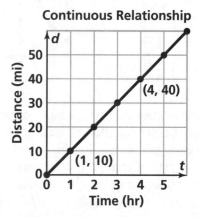

Continuous Relationship

In a distance/time/rate situation, students are asked to decide whether the points can be connected and if so, how they can be connected. For example, the points representing the time and distance of a cyclist can be connected in many ways. A straight segment connecting two points implies that the cyclist traveled at a constant rate in the time interval between the points. The four graphs below show other ways two points may be connected.

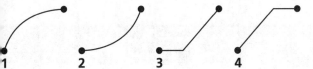

- Graph 1 shows the cyclist starting fast and then gradually slowing down.
- Graph 2 shows the cyclist starting slowly and then gradually speeding up.
- Graph 3 shows the cyclist not moving for the first part of the time interval, and then riding at a steady rate for the rest.
- Graph 4 shows the cyclist riding at a steady rate for the first part of the time interval and stopped for the rest.

Selecting a Scale

Another aspect of graphing is that of scale. This is closely connected to the range of values for each variable. To represent a relationship graphically, students must have a good feel for the range of values. Students must select an appropriate scale so that the relevant pieces of the graph can be displayed. The effects of the scale can often lead to distortion in the interpretation as shown in the graphs below. For example, suppose students select a scale of 0 to 10 for both axes when they graph the equation $d = 10t$, as in Graph A. Only the information about the first hour would be shown on this graph. This may not be enough information for students to understand the relationship. The scale in Graph B may lead students to believe that the distance covered in three hours is minimal. Graph C best represents the situation.

Graph A

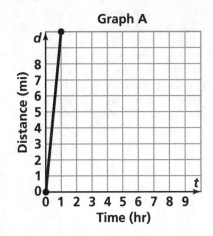

Graph B

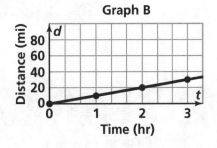

Graph C

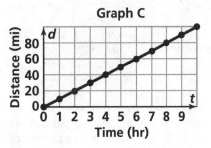

Equations

Students develop strategies for writing symbolic equations to represent simple relationships between quantitative variables. The value of an equation is that it is brief and represents a complete picture of the pattern, while tables and graphs can show only parts of the relationships.

While relationships between variables are the most important idea in this unit, it is the representation of these relationships that is the dominant theme. It is important for students to move freely among the various representations. It may not be obvious initially to students how the entries in a table relate to points on a graph or to solutions of a symbolic equation; and conversely, how solutions to an equation or points on a graph relate to entries in the table; however, these connections are explored in depth in this unit.

By the end of the unit, students should feel very comfortable with tables and graphs and with some simple equations. Students should also have an appreciation of the advantages and disadvantages of each representation.

In this unit, students write equations for relationships within a context. They can use the words or clues in the context to represent the relationship as a symbolic statement or equation.

Big Idea	Prior Work	Future Work
Collecting, organizing, and representing data about the relationship between two variables	Gathering data by conducting trials of an experiment or game; organizing data in tables and graphs in order to look for patterns and relationships (*Data About Us; How Likely Is It?*)	Analyzing patterns to develop concepts of surface area and volume (*Filling and Wrapping*); studying data to develop the concept of linear, exponential, and quadratic functions (*Moving Straight Ahead; Growing, Growing, Growing; Frogs, Fleas, and Painted Cubes*); gathering and analyzing data about populations (*Samples and Populations*)
Identifying patterns and extreme values in data organized in graphs or tables; making inferences about situations based on such information	Identifying patterns in number and geometry (*Prime Time; Shapes and Designs*); analyzing maximum and minimum values in measurement (*Covering and Surrounding*)	Understanding relationships between edge lengths and surface area and volume of three-dimensional figures (*Stretching and Shrinking, Filling and Wrapping*); identifying maximum and minimum values for a mathematical model or equation (*Thinking with Mathematical Models; Frogs, Fleas, and Painted Cubes*)
Analyzing a pattern or relationship in a graph or table to identify variables and interpret the relationship between variables, particularly how variables change relative to one another	Organizing, displaying, and interpreting data in one- and two-dimensional graphs and tables (*Data About Us*); constructing graphs of the relationship between the dimensions and area of a rectangle when the perimeter is held constant and between the dimensions and perimeter when the area is held constant (*Covering and Surrounding*)	Extending tables and graphs to include negative coordinates and quantities (*Accentuate the Negative*); formalizing understandings of linear equations in $y = mx + b$ form (*Moving Straight Ahead*); studying and developing mathematical models (*Thinking with Mathematical Models*); identifying and studying nonlinear patterns of growth (*Growing, Growing, Growing; Frogs, Fleas, and Painted Cubes*)
Analyzing simple linear relationships and expressing them as written and symbolic rules	Developing operation algorithms for fractions, decimals, and percents (*Bits and Pieces II; Bits and Pieces III*); developing rules for perimeter (*Covering and Surrounding*)	Expressing linear relationships in $y = mx + b$ form (*Moving Straight Ahead*); describing situations with linear models or equations (*Thinking with Mathematical Models*); developing strategies for expressing linear relationships in symbols and for solving linear equations (*Say It With Symbols*); developing strategies for solving simultaneous linear equations (*The Shapes of Algebra*)
Using graphing calculators to organize and represent data and to analyze linear relationships	Using four-function calculators for computation	Using graphing calculators to graph and compare lines (*Moving Straight Ahead*); using graphing calculators to develop and study mathematical models (*Thinking with Mathematical Models*); performing isometries in two dimensions (*Kaleidoscopes, Hubcaps, and Mirrors*)

Planning for the Unit

Pacing Suggestions and Materials

Investigations and Assessments	Pacing 45–50 min. classes	Materials for Students	Materials for Teachers
1 Variables, Tables, and Coordinate Graphs	6 days	Clock or watch with second hand, large sheets of paper (optional)	Transparent grids, Transparencies 1.3A, 1.3B, 1.4 (optional)
Mathematical Reflections	$\frac{1}{2}$ day		
Assessment: Check Up 1	$\frac{1}{2}$ day		
2 Analyzing Graphs and Tables	4 days	Transparent grids	Transparencies 2.1A, 2.2B, 2.2, 2.3
Mathematical Reflections	$\frac{1}{2}$ day		
Assessment: Check Up 2	$\frac{1}{2}$ day		
3 Rules and Equations	4 days	Colored pens, pencils, or markers; transparent grids	Transparencies 3.1, 3.2. and 3.3 (optional)
Mathematical Reflections	$\frac{1}{2}$ day		
Assessment: Partner Quiz	1 day		
4 Calculator Tables and Graphs	4 days	Graphing calculators	Overhead graphing calculator (optional), Graphing calculator linking cable and software, such as TI-GraphLink™ (optional) Transparencies 4.1, 4.2A, and 4.2B (optional)
Mathematical Reflections	$\frac{1}{2}$ day		
Looking Back and Looking Ahead	1 day		
Assessment: Self Assessment	Take Home		
Assessment: Unit Test	1 day		

Total Time	24 days	Materials for Use in All Investigations	
For detailed pacing for Problems within each Investigation, see the Suggested Pacing at the beginning of each Investigation.		Calculators, grid paper, blank transparencies and transparency markers (optional), student notebooks	Blank transparencies and transparency markers (optional)

For detailed pacing for Problems within each Investigation, see the Suggested Pacing at the beginning of each Investigation.

For pacing with block scheduling, see next page.

Pacing for Block Scheduling (90-minute class periods)

Investigation	Suggested Pacing	Investigation	Suggested Pacing
Investigation 1	**3 days**	**Investigation 3**	**2 days**
Problem 1.1	$\frac{1}{2}$ day	Problem 3.1	$\frac{1}{2}$ day
Problem 1.2	$\frac{1}{2}$ day	Problem 3.2	$\frac{1}{2}$ day
Problem 1.3	$\frac{1}{2}$ day	Problem 3.3	$\frac{1}{2}$ day
Problem 1.4	$\frac{1}{2}$ day	Math Reflections	$\frac{1}{2}$ day
Problem 1.5	$\frac{1}{2}$ day	**Investigation 4**	**2 days**
Math Reflections	$\frac{1}{2}$ day	Problem 4.1	$\frac{1}{2}$ day
Investigation 2	**2 days**	Problem 4.2	$\frac{1}{2}$ day
Problem 2.1	$\frac{1}{2}$ day	Problem 4.3	$\frac{1}{2}$ day
Problem 2.2	$\frac{1}{2}$ day	Math Reflections	$\frac{1}{2}$ day
Problem 2.3	$\frac{1}{2}$ day		
Math Reflections	$\frac{1}{2}$ day		

Vocabulary

Essential Terms Developed in This Unit		Useful Terms Referenced in This Unit	Terms Developed in Previous Units
change	scale	plot	area
coordinate graph	table	point	circumference
coordinate pair	variable	range of values	diameter
dependent variable	*x*-axis		line plot
distance/time/rate of speed	*x*-coordinate		mean
equation, formula	*y*-axis		median
income/cost/profit	*y*-coordinate		mode
independent variable			perimeter
pattern			radius
relationship			range
rule			symbolic form
			polygon

-Go Online

For: Multiple-Choice Skills Practice
Web Code: ank-5500

Components

Use the chart below to quickly see which components are available for each Investigation.

Investigation	Labsheets	Additional Practice	Transparencies		Formal Assessment		Assessment Options	
			Problem	Summary	Check Up	Partner Quiz	Multiple-Choice	Question Bank
1		✔	1.3A, 1.3B, 1.4		✔		✔	✔
2		✔	2.1A, 2.1B, 2.2, 2.3		✔		✔	✔
3		✔	3.1, 3.2, 3.3			✔	✔	✔
4		✔	4.1, 4.2A, 4.2B				✔	✔
For the Unit	Centimeter Grid Paper	*ExamView* CD-ROM, Web site	LBLA		Unit Test, Notebook Check, Self Assessment		Multiple-Choice Items, Question Bank, *ExamView* CD-ROM	

Also Available For Use With This Unit

- Parent Guide: take-home letter for the unit
- Implementing CMP
- Spanish Assessment Resources
- Additional online and technology resources

Technology

The Use of Calculators

Connected Mathematics was developed with the belief that calculators should always be available and that students should learn when their use is appropriate. In the first three investigations, the calculations involve only simple arithmetic, so when calculators are needed, nonscientific calculators are adequate.

The graphing calculator is introduced in Investigation 4. This tool allows students to look at many examples quickly and helps them observe patterns and make conjectures about functions. In the teaching notes, examples using the Texas Instruments TI-83 calculator show teachers how to help students use the graphing calculators. If you have a different type of graphing calculators, see the calculator's reference manual for instructions.

Bringing graphing calculators into the classroom creates some management issues. If you have several classes using the same calculator, you will need to develop a systematic way to deal with calculator damage and missing calculators. In general, students are happy to have access to graphing calculators and do not want to lose that privilege. For this reason, most teachers have had fewer problems with loss or destruction of graphing calculators than with loss or destruction of textbooks and other supplies.

Management ideas that have worked well for other teachers include these tips.

- Send a note to parents at the beginning of the unit. Tell them that graphing calculators are being used in the mathematics class and explain that their teenagers are responsible for the care of these tools when using them. Have parents sign the note accepting responsibility for damaged or missing calculators. Do not allow students to use the calculators until the note is returned to you.

- Engrave all calculators with the school name and an individual number. You may be able to borrow an engraving tool from the local police department.

- Assign a numbered calculator to each student. Each day the student must use the calculator with his or her designated number. If there is damage, the student must report it to the teacher at the beginning of the hour.

- Have students clear the memory of their calculators at the end of each class. Be aware that doing this will erase any programs downloaded into the calculator.

- Establish a rule that no students may leave the room at the end of the period until all calculators are checked, counted, and stored.

- Develop a storage system so that you can tell at a glance whether all calculators are in place at the end of the period.

Student Interactivity CD-ROM

Includes interactive activities to enhance the learning in the Problems within Investigations.

PHSchool.com

For Students Multiple-choice practice with instant feedback, updated data sources, data sets for Tinkerplots data software.

For Teachers Professional development, curriculum support, downloadable forms, and more.

See also www.math.msu.edu/cmp for more resources for both teachers and students.

ExamView® CD-ROM

Create multiple versions of practice sheets and tests for course objectives and standardized tests. Includes dynamic questions, online testing, student reports, and all test and practice items in Spanish. Also includes all items in the *Assessment Resources* and *Additional Practice*.

Teacher Express™ CD-ROM

Includes a lesson planning tool, the Teacher's Guide pages, and all the teaching resources.

LessonLab Online Courses

LessonLab offers comprehensive, facilitated professional development designed to help teachers implement CMP2 and improve student achievement. To learn more, please visit PHSchool.com/cmp2

Assessment Summary

Ongoing Informal Assessment

Embedded in the Student Unit

Problems Use students' work from the Problems to informally check student understanding.

ACE exercises Use ACE exercises for homework assignments to assess student understanding.

Mathematical Reflections Have students summarize their learning at the end of each Investigation.

Looking Back and Looking Ahead At the end of the unit, use the first two sections to allow students to show what they know about the unit.

Additional Resources

Teacher's Guide Use the Check for Understanding feature of some Summaries and the probing questions that appear in the *Launch, Explore,* or *Summarize* sections of all Investigations to check student understanding.

Summary Transparencies Use these transparencies to focus class attention on a summary check for understanding.

Self Assessment

Notebook Check Students use this tool to organize and check their notebooks before giving them to their teacher. Located in *Assessment Resources*.

Self Assessment At the end of the unit, students reflect on and provide examples of what they learned. Located in *Assessment Resources*.

Formal Assessment

Choose the assessment materials that are appropriate for your students.

Assessment	For Use After	Focus	Student Work
Check Up 1	Invest. 1	Skills	Individual
Check Up 2	Invest. 2	Skills	Individual
Partner Quiz	Invest. 3	Rich problems	Pair
Unit Test	The Unit	Skills, rich problems	Individual

Additional Resources

Multiple-Choice Items Use these items for home-work, review, a quiz, or add them to the Unit Test.

Question Bank Choose from these questions for homework, review, or replacements for Quiz, Check Up, or Unit Test questions.

Additional Practice Choose practice exercises for each Investigation for homework, review, or formal assessments.

***ExamView* CD-ROM** Create practice sheets, review quizzes, and tests with this dynamic software. Give online tests and receive student progress reports. *(All test items are also available in Spanish.)*

Spanish Assessment Resources

Includes Partner Quizzes, Check Ups, Unit Test, Multiple-Choice Items, Question Bank, Notebook Check, and Self Assessment. Plus, the *ExamView* CD-ROM has all test items in Spanish.

Correlation to Standardized Tests

Investigation	NAEP	Terra Nova CAT6	CTBS	ITBS	SAT10	Local Test
1 Variables, Tables, and Coordinate Graphs	A4c, A4d	✔	✔		✔	
2 Analyzing Graphs and Tables	A2b, A3a	✔		✔	✔	
3 Rules and Equations	A4a, A4c	✔	✔	✔	✔	
4 Calculator Tables and Graphs	A1a, A1b, Aic	✔	✔	✔	✔	

NAEP National Assessment of Educational Progress   **CAT6/Terra Nova** California Achievement Test, 6th Ed.   **ITBS** Iowa Test of Basic Skills, Form M
CTBS/Terra Nova Comprehensive Test of Basic Skills   **SAT10** Stanford Achievement Test, 10th Ed.

Introducing Your Students to *Variables and Patterns*

One way to introduce *Variables and Patterns* is by asking students to make a list of things about themselves and the world that change. You might give them a few suggestions, such as the length of their hair and the temperature. After a few minutes, have students share some of their ideas as you list them on the board. Explain to students that things that change are called *variables*.

Choose some of the variables on the list and ask students to describe how the variables change and what things affect the change. For example, hair length increases slowly and steadily, then decreases suddenly when students get a hair cut, and then increases steadily again.

Tell your students that, in *Variables and Patterns*, they will explore variables and how two variables change relative to one another. They will make tables and graphs to help them understand how variables are related, and, in some cases, they will write equations to represent relationships.

Using the Unit Opener

Refer students to the three questions posed on the opening page of the Student Edition. You may want to have a class discussion about these questions, but do not worry about finding the "correct" answer at this time. Each question is posed again in the investigations, at the time when the students have learned the mathematical concepts required to answer it. Ask your students to keep these questions in mind as they work through the investigations and to think about how they might use the ideas they are learning to help them determine the answers.

Mathematical Highlights

The Mathematical Highlights page in the student edition provides information to students, parents, and other family members. It gives students a preview of the mathematics and some of the overarching questions that they should ask themselves while studying *Variables and Patterns*.

As they work through the unit, students can refer back to the Mathematical Highlights page to review what they have learned and to preview what is still to come. This page also tells students' families what mathematical ideas and activities will be covered as the class works through *Variables and Patterns*.

Connected Mathematics 2™

Variables and Patterns

Introducing Algebra

Glenda Lappan
James T. Fey
William M. Fitzgerald
Susan N. Friel
Elizabeth Difanis Phillips

PEARSON

Boston, Massachusetts · Glenview, Illinois · Shoreview, Minnesota · Upper Saddle River, New Jersey

Notes _____

_____

_____

_____

Variables and Patterns

How does the number of daylight hours change with the passage of time in a year? Why does this happen?

Who offers the better deal for renting a truck? *East Coast Trucks:* $4.25 for each mile driven or *Philadelphia Truck Rental:* $200 plus $2 per mile driven.

The group admission price for Wild World Amusement park is $50, plus $10 per person. What equation relates the price to the number of people in the group?

2 Variables and Patterns

Notes _____

_____

_____

_____

Some things never seem to change. The sun always rises in the east and sets in the west. The United States holds a presidential election every four years. Labor Day always falls on the first Monday of September.

But many other things are always changing. Temperatures rise and fall within a day and from season to season. Store sales change in response to rising and falling prices and shopper demand. Audiences for television shows and movies change as viewers' interests change. The speeds of cars on streets and highways change in response to variations in traffic density and road conditions.

In mathematics, science, and business, quantities that change are called *variables*. Many problems require predicting how changes in the values of one variable are related to changes in the values of another. To help you solve such problems, you can represent the relationships between variables using word descriptions, tables, graphs, and equations. The mathematical ideas and skills used to solve such problems come from the branch of mathematics called *algebra*. This unit introduces some of the basic tools of algebra.

Notes

Mathematical Highlights

Introducing Algebra

In *Variables and Patterns,* you will study some basic ideas of algebra and learn some ways to use those ideas.

You will learn how to

- Identify variables in situations
- Recognize situations in which changes in variables are related in useful patterns
- Describe patterns of change shown in words, tables, and graphs
- Construct tables and graphs to display relationships between variables
- Observe how a change in the relationship between two variables affects the table, graph, and equation
- Use algebraic symbols to write equations relating variables
- Use tables, graphs, and equations to solve problems
- Use graphing calculators to construct tables and graphs of relationships between variables and to answer questions about these relationships

As you work on problems in this unit, ask yourself questions about problem situations that involve related quantitative variables:

What are the variables in the problem?

Which variables depend on, or change in relation to, others?

How can I use a table, graph, or equation to display and analyze a relationship between quantitative variables?

What does it mean when I see regular and predictable changes in a table of data or a graph?

How can I use these regular or predictable changes to make estimates or predictions about other data values?

Notes _____

_____

_____

_____

Investigation 1 Variables, Tables, and Coordinate Graphs

Mathematical and Problem-Solving Goals

- Collect experimental data and organize it in a table
- Identify patterns and relationships between variables using information in a table
- Create a coordinate graph of data in a table
- Identify patterns and relationships between variables using information in a graph
- Compare table and graph representations of the same data
- Consider data values between plotted points
- Create a table from data in a coordinate graph
- Compare patterns of change in a table and graph
- Interpret narrative notes to make a table and a graph

Summary of Problems

Problem 1.1 Preparing for a Bicycle Tour

Students perform an experiment involving jumping jacks and collect the data in a table. They then analyze and interpret the pattern of change in the table.

Problem 1.2 Making Graphs

Students are introduced to variables and coordinate graphs as they graph their data from Problem 1.1.

Problem 1.3 Day 1: Atlantic City to Lewes

Students graph data in a table and interpret their graphs. They consider values between plotted points and think about when it may be useful to connect plotted points.

Problem 1.4 Day 2: Lewes to Chincoteague Island

Students interpret a graph, make a table based on the graph, and compare the usefulness of the two representations.

Problem 1.5 Day 3: Chincoteague Island to Norfolk

Students make a table and graph from a narrative. They also compute average speed.

	Suggested Pacing	Materials for Students	Materials for Teachers	ACE Assignments
All	$6\frac{1}{2}$ days		Transparent grids	
1.1	1 day	Clock or watch with second hand	Transparencies 1.1A and 1.1B	13–17
1.2	1 day	Grid paper		1–3, 18–20
1.3	$1\frac{1}{2}$ days	Grid paper	Transparencies 1.3A, 1.3B, (optional) 1.3C	4, 5, 26
1.4	$1\frac{1}{2}$ days		Transparency 1.4 (optional)	6–9, 21–24, 27, 28
1.5	1 day	Grid paper, large sheets of paper (optional)	Transparency 1.5	10–12, 25, 29, 30
MR	$\frac{1}{2}$ day			

1.1 Preparing for a Bicycle Tour

Goals

- Collect experimental data and organize it in a table

- Identify patterns and relationships between variables using information in a table

In *Variables and Patterns,* students explore the idea of variables and how two variables change relative to each other. They look for relationships and patterns of change between two variables. In this investigation, students investigate the relationship between elapsed time and the number of jumping jacks they can do.

Launch 1.1

Tell the class about bicycles and the yearly bicycle tour across Iowa. Encourage students to share other facts about organized bicycle tours they might know. Then continue reading about the bicycle trip that the five college students are planning. Have students share their ideas about the questions in the Getting Ready. Students should justify their guesses about the distance they think they could ride in a day and consider ways in which their speed might vary throughout the day.

- *How far do you think you could ride in a day?* (Answers will vary.)

- *How do you think the speed of your ride would change during the course of the day?* (Most students will indicate that their speed would slow down over the course of the day as they grew fatigued. Others might say that they could get surges of energy, especially towards the end.)

- *What conditions would affect the speed and distance you could ride?* (Answers might include the type of terrain (rocky or smooth); how much of the ride is uphill, downhill, or flat; weather conditions and temperature; and how much gear the riders carry.)

After a short class discussion, move on to the stamina experiment. Connect the bike tour and

the jumping jack experiment by pointing out that both activities involve physical exertion over a period of time. This experiment works best if students are divided into groups of four. Within the group, each student has a job: performing jumping jacks, counting jumps, timing when 10 seconds have passed, and recording the number of jumping jacks completed at the end of every 10 seconds for the 2-minute time period.

The directions suggest that students do jumping jacks for 2 minutes. If the time limit is too short (say only 1 minute), then the jumping jack rate is not as likely to change. Two minutes has worked well in many classes. We suggest that you tell students to talk to you if they are not physically able to do the experiment. Inform everyone that if they get tired they should stop. Every student does *not* need to jump.

You may wish to have a group of four students model the experiment in order to describe and clarify the roles of each person in the group. Emphasize the following points:

- The *jumper* performs a complete jumping jack when he or she completes these three steps:

  1. Start with feet together and hands at sides.

  2. Jump, landing with legs apart and hands touching above the head.

  3. Jump again, returning to the starting position with feet together and hands at sides.

- The *counter* counts an additional jump each time the jumper returns to the starting position.

- The *timer* calls out "time" when each 10 seconds passes.

- The *recorder* listens for the timer to call "time" and then writes the last number the counter called into the table.

Suggest that students make a table with the times from 10 seconds to 120 seconds, listed in 10-second intervals, *before* conducting the experiment. After the demonstration, have students perform the experiment and then complete Problem 1.1. Students can work in groups of four to gather the data. Have as many students as possible take a turn at each task. Remind them that they need to count and record the *total* number of jumping jacks their teammates complete by the end of each time interval.

Explore 1.1

As students work, verify their understanding of each role's function.

When groups are finished, give them time to make a copy of each jumper's data for each person who jumped. Encourage students to discuss within their group possible explanations for what they see in their tables. Students should consider all the data sets when answering.

The data students collected for Problem 1.1 are used in Problem 1.2. Be sure to have students keep a record of their own data.

Summarize 1.1

Have groups share their findings about rates of jumping jacks. Some groups may want to share all or part of their data on the board to help them make a point. Ask what the jumping jack experiment suggests about bicycle-riding speed over time. (Usually the rate decreases as time passes.)

Suggested Questions Ask students to review the process of making a table to record data. Ask:

- *The instructions told you to use 10-second intervals. Could you have chosen a different time interval for recording data in your table?*

- *Would your choice have affected your observations in Question B? If so, in what way?*

1.1 Preparing for a Bicycle Tour

Mathematical Goals

- Collect experimental data and organize it in a table
- Identify patterns and relationships between variables using information in a table

Launch

Tell the class about bicycles and bicycle tours. Read about the bicycle trip that the five college students are planning. Discuss the questions in the Getting Ready.

- *How far do you think you could ride in a day?*
- *How do you think the speed of your ride would change during the course of the day?*
- *What conditions would affect the speed and distance you could ride?*

Divide students into groups of four for the stamina experiment. Make sure students understand the four tasks: jumper, timer, counter, recorder. Have students perform the experiment and then complete Problem 1.1. Have each student take a turn at each task. Suggest that they organize their table in 10-second intervals.

Materials
- Clock or watch with second hand
- Transparencies 1.1A and 1.1B

Explore

When groups are finished, give them time to make a copy of the data for each person in their group, as the data in Problem 1.1 are used in Problem 1.2.

Encourage students to discuss within their group possible explanations for what they see in their tables. Students should consider all four data sets when answering.

Summarize

Have groups share their findings about rates of jumping jacks. Ask what the jumping jack experiment suggests about bicycle-riding speed over time. (Usually the rate decreases as time passes.)

Ask students to review the process of making a table to record data.

- *The instructions told you to use 10-second intervals. Could you have chosen a different time interval for recording data in your table?*
- *Would your choice have affected your observations in Question B? If so, in what way?*

Materials
- Student notebooks

Vocabulary
- table

ACE Assignment Guide for Problem 1.1

Other *Connections* 13–17

Adapted For suggestions about adapting ACE exercises, see the *CMP Special Needs Handbook.*
Connecting to Prior Units 13–15: *Bits and Pieces I*

Answers to Problem 1.1

A. Student data will vary. In one class, several students started jumping at a rate of 10 jumping jacks for every 10 seconds. After 1 minute, they started to slow down slightly. Many had data entries of 107 and 108 jumping jacks for 120 seconds.

B. Some students will have data that show their jumping jack rate decreases as time passes. Even though the total number of jumps increases for each 10-second interval in the table, the rate decreases since the number of jumps in each 10-second interval decreases as time passes.

C. This pattern suggests that the bike-riding speed would probably decrease somewhat over a day's time.

Making Graphs

Goals

- Create a coordinate graph of data in a table

- Identify patterns and relationships between variables using information in a graph

- Compare table and graph representations of the same data

In this problem, students learn how to make coordinate graphs. Additionally, they compare a table and graph that represent the same information. This helps students see which aspects of a data set each representation best reveals. For example, a table shows exact data values, while a graph makes it easier to see overall trends in the data.

Launch 1.2

Problem 1.2 uses the data collected from Problem 1.1. This problem asks students to look at the jumping jack information in another way, by constructing a coordinate graph

Suggested Questions You may wish to review coordinate graphs by asking questions such as the following:

- *What does a coordinate graph look like?* (a grid with points that represent pairs of related numerical data; the *x*-axis represents one variable and the *y*-axis represents the other)

- *What is the purpose of a coordinate graph?* (to show a relationship between two variables)

- *How do you locate points on a coordinate graph?* (Locate the *x*-value on the *x*-axis and draw an imaginary line perpendicular to the *x*-axis from that point. Repeat with the *y*-value and the *y*-axis. Make the point where the imaginary lines intersect.)

If your students used *Connected Mathematics* in grade 6, remind them that these ideas were introduced in the *Data About Us* unit.

Go over the introduction to Problem 1.2, which gives the steps for making a coordinate graph.

Because a goal of this problem is for students to learn how to make a coordinate graph of a relationship between variables, you might want to walk through the steps with the whole class. You can use a transparent grid to demonstrate.

Suggested Questions

- *What are the variables in this situation?* (Time and Number of Jumping Jacks)

- *Which variable is the independent variable and which is the dependent variable?* (Time is customarily considered the independent variable. In this case, the number of jumping jacks depends on the time, so it makes sense that the number of jumping jacks is the dependent variable.)

- *Which variable should we put on each axis so we can best see the "story" the graph tells?* (Convention suggests using the *x*-axis for time and *y*-axis for distance. This lets us see how the "story" unfolds over time as we read the graph from left to right.)

- *What values should be represented by the grid marks, or tic-marks, on the x-axis?* (Because a jumping-jacks value was recorded every 10 seconds, it makes sense to label the tic mark on the *x*-axis in intervals of 10 seconds.)

- *If I did 97 jumping jacks, how do you think I should label the tic marks on the y-axis?* (Possible answer: You could label the tic marks in intervals of 10 jumping jacks.)

- *How do we make points on the graph to represent the jumping jack value for each time?* [Each (*time, jumping jacks*) pair recorded in the table is a coordinate pair. Start at the time value on the *x*-axis and follow a line up. Start at the jumping jacks value on the *y*-axis and follow a line right. Make a point where the lines intersect.]

Ask students to think individually about Problem 1.2 for a few minutes. Then, pair them with a partner to compare strategies and find a solution. Finally, have students discuss answers in a group of four. Each student needs to learn to make a graph and think about what a graph indicates about the data.

Explore 1.2

Have students construct graphs using their jumping jack data (either on large sheets of grid paper or on transparent grids for sharing during the summary). When students have completed their graphs, have them record their answers and explanations for Questions B and C.

As you move around the room, find and help students who have little experience with making graphs.

Suggested Questions As students begin to finish their graphs, ask questions such as these:

- *How did you choose the labels for your axes?*

- *What would be a good title for this graph?*

- *Why does a graph need a title and axis labels?*

- *Were you surprised by the pattern in the graph? If so, in what way? If not, how did you know what to expect?*

Summarize 1.2

These examples can be used to enhance student discussion and address difficulties students are having. Point out things that the presenters did correctly, and allow other students to ask them questions about their graphs.

Suggested Questions You might display one of the graphs students made and ask these questions:

- *Which variable is on the* x-*axis?* (time)

- *Why does it make sense to put time on the* x-*axis?* (because it is the independent variable; because as we read the graph from left to right, we can see how the number of jumping jacks changes as time passes)

- *What is the least value on the* x-*axis?* (0. Some students may say the least value should be 10 instead of 0. This question gives you an opportunity to have students think about why 0 needs to be on the axis. Time 0 represents what action is taking place at the start of the experiment. In this case, there are 0 jumping jacks at time 0.)

- *What is the greatest value on the* x-*axis?* (120)

- *Why is it reasonable to have the scale go from 0 to 120?* (because that is the amount of time we spent counting jumping jacks from start to finish)

- *What is the size of the interval for the* x-*axis scale?* (10 seconds)

- *Why is it reasonable that the interval be 10 seconds?* (Because we collected data in intervals of 10 seconds.)

- *Which variable is on the* y-*axis?* (number of jumping jacks)

- *What is the least value on the* y-*axis?* (0) *What is the greatest value on the* y-*axis? Did everyone have the same greatest value? Why or why not?* (probably not, because students did different numbers of jumping jacks)

- *What is the size of the interval for the* y-*axis scale? Did everyone use that size interval?* (Answers will vary depending on data and preference. Many students will use intervals of 10.)

- *What do you think would happen to this graph if we changed the size of the interval? For example, what would happen to the graph if we used intervals of 5 jumping jacks instead of 10?* (The steepness of the graph would change.)

You may wish to prepare a transparent grid that shows several graphs of the same data with different axes ranges and scales or overlay some of the student graphs.

Question C asks students about relationships. This is probably a new usage of this word for most students. You will want to find ways to use the word *relationship* when discussing tables and graphs in the future. Students might not have much to say about this idea so early in the unit. If no one has any comments, model the process of looking at a relationship between variables. You might say, "In the table, the numbers are easy to read, and it is easy for me to calculate the number of jumps for each 10-second interval. But it is easier for me to see when the person started to slow down by looking at the graph. I see that the graph is getting less steep near the end of the time period. The jumper was probably slowing down because he or she was tired."

1.2 Making Graphs

Mathematical Goals

- Create a coordinate graph of data in a table
- Identify patterns and relationships between variables using information in a graph
- Compare table and graph representations of the same data

Launch

Review coordinate graphs.

- *What does a coordinate graph look like?*
- *What is the purpose of a coordinate graph?*
- *How do you locate points on a coordinate graph?*

Walk students through the steps in the student book for making a coordinate graph. Let students work in pairs and then share their work in a larger group of four to six.

Materials
- Transparent grid (optional)

Vocabulary
- variable
- coordinate graph
- dependent variable
- *x*-axis
- *y*-axis
- range
- scale
- coordinate pair

Explore

Have students construct a coordinate graph of jumping jack data, and then answer Questions B and C.

- *How did you choose the labels for your axes?*
- *What would be a good title for this graph?*
- *Why does a graph need a title and axis labels?*
- *Were you surprised by the pattern in the graph? If so, in what way? If not, how did you know what to expect?*

Materials
- Transparent grid

Summarize

Have a few students present their graphs. Point out things presenters did correctly, and address difficulties students are having. Allow other students to ask questions.

Display one of the graphs and ask the following questions:

- *Which variable is on the x-axis? Why does it make sense to put time on the x-axis?*
- *What is the least value on the x-axis? What is the greatest value on the x-axis? Why is it reasonable to have the scale go from 0 to 120?*
- *What is the size of the interval for the x-axis scale? Why is it reasonable that the interval be 10 seconds?*

Materials
- Transparent grid (optional)
- Student notebooks

Vocabulary
- relationship

continued on next page

- *Which variable is on the y-axis? What is the least value on the y-axis? What is the greatest value? Did everyone have the same greatest value? Why or why not?*

- *What is the size of the interval for the y-axis scale? Did everyone have that size interval? Why or why not?*

- *What do you think would happen to this graph if we changed the size of the interval? For example, what would happen to the graph if we used intervals of 5 jumping jacks instead of 10?*

Discuss the idea of a relationship between variables. You might model the process of looking at and discussing relationships in a table and graph.

ACE Assignment Guide for Problem 1.2

Core 1–3
Other *Connections* 18–20; unassigned choices from earlier problems

Adapted For suggestions about adapting ACE exercises, see the *CMP Special Needs Handbook.*
Connecting to Prior Units 18–20: *How Likely Is It?*

Answers to Problem 1.2

A. Answers will vary. Sample graph:

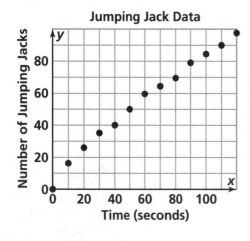

B. Answers will vary. The graph above shows that, while the total number of jumping jacks increases over time, for most intervals, the number of jumps in a 10-second interval decreases over time. Be sure students understand the graph shows this because the vertical distance between adjacent points becomes smaller as time passes. This may be hard for students now, but they will see the same concept in future problems, when they look at how distance changes over time.

C. Answers will vary. Students might note that they can see the exact numbers in the table and therefore more easily see that the jumper is slowing down. Other students might prefer the visual image of the graph. The graph gives the whole picture of the data in a glance so that changes can easily be seen.

Goals

- Create a coordinate graph of data in a table
- Consider data values between plotted points
- Compare table and graph representations of the same data

This problem asks students to make a graph from data presented in a table. Making the graph reinforces graphing skills and helps students see the relationship between the table and graph representations of the same data. Students look for patterns of change in the data, and think about how these changes show up in a table and in a graph. They also consider the advantages and disadvantages of each representation. As students gain experience in looking for patterns of change in data, they will develop the ability to ask relevant questions that guide them in their analysis.

Launch 1.3

Tell the class about Sidney's, Liz's, Celia's, Malcolm's, and Theo's plans to test their tour and about the first day of their ride. Have students look at the table (time, distance) data collected on Day 1.

Tell students they will be making a coordinate graph of the data. You may wish to review the decisions students need to make to make their graphs. For example, they must determine which variable to put on each axis and choose reasonable scales. Based on the discussion for Problem 1.2, students should be able to explain that time is usually put on the *x*-axis. This allows the graph to tell a story of how a variable changes over time as we read from left to right.

Read Problem 1.3 with students. When students understand the problem and what it is asking, let them work in small groups or pairs. Each student should make a graph and answer the questions.

Explore 1.3

As you visit groups, determine who is still having difficulties with graphing by examining each student's work and by noting how much each student depends on other group members for help.

Suggested Questions You can ask questions such as the following to help students focus on what the data show:

- *What are the variables?* (time and distance)
- *Which variable goes on which axis?*
- *What intervals can you use?*
- *What happens between 3.5 and 4.5 hours?* (Distance did not change. They may have stopped for lunch.)
- *How is this interval (or the lunch stop) shown in the graph?* (In the graph, it is shown by 3 points on the same horizontal line. The vertical distance between the points doesn't change, indicating that the students were stopped.)
- *Do you think they got tired as the day progressed? Explain.* (They seemed to slow down and then have a burst of speed just before lunch.)

Have some groups put their graphs on a transparent grid to share during the summary.

Summarize 1.3

Display Transparency 1.3B. Have students discuss the scales, axis labels, and titles and the importance of these elements to the graph.

Suggested Questions

- *Which variable is displayed on the x-axis?* (time) *Why?* (Time is usually put on the x-axis so that the graph tells a story of how a variable changes over time as we read from left to right. Also, it is the independent variable and thus should go on the x-axis.)
- *What is the least value on the x-axis?* (0) *What is the greatest value on the x-axis?* (5)
- *Why is it reasonable to have the size of the interval for the x-axis be 0.5 hours?* (The data were collected on half-hour intervals.)
- *Which variable is displayed on the y-axis?* (distance)
- *What is the least value on the y-axis?* (0) *What is the greatest value on the y-axis?* (45)

- *What is the size of the interval for the y-axis on this graph?* (5 miles)

- *Did anyone use an interval other than 5 miles for the y-axis?* (If yes, have students share and explain why this size is reasonable. Ask how this new scale affects the appearance of the graph.)

Have students share their answers to the questions in the problem. Parts (1) and (2) of Question B require students to read data values from the graph and think about values between plotted points. Ask students what it means if two points are connected with a line segment and in what types of situations connecting plotted points makes sense.

When line segments are used to connect points, an assumption is made that the change from one data point to the next happens at a constant rate. Part (3) of Question B introduces the idea that the rate of change between two points does not have to be constant. This is a difficult concept for many students. It is worth spending time discussing these ideas throughout the unit. When matching the paths with the statements, students may question why statement (a) does not correspond to path (iii) and statement (d) does not correspond to path (iv). Emphasize that the horizontal segment in these paths means the distance is not increasing and therefore the rider is not moving at all. Students may ask, "Why does the line go on if the rider is not moving?" Point out that, even though the rider is not moving, time continues to pass. Therefore, the segment gives us information about how long the rider was stopped. You may want to ask students to describe another situation that matches one of the graphs.

Have some students share the descriptions they wrote for Question C. After each description, ask students to identify patterns of change, and give possible reasons for the changes. Variables such as terrain, wind speed, food and rest breaks, and temperature should be mentioned as possible explanations for the data changes. If students do not use the word *variable* to describe the things that might have affected the riders' speed and distance traveled, make sure you add this word to the conversation. Also, let the class ask questions of each presenter and decide whether the presenter's story fits or goes beyond the data given. Compare the different descriptions given by presenters.

Question D requires students to think about the strengths and weaknesses of the table and graph representations. Have students share their ideas. For example, a graph shows the sizes of changes in the data at a glance but does not pinpoint exact numerical changes. The table can be better for analyzing exact changes in the data, although it does not always show the sizes of the changes at a glance.

1.3 Day 1: Atlantic City to Lewes

Mathematical Goals

- Create a coordinate graph of data in a table
- Consider data values between plotted points
- Compare table and graph representations of the same data

Launch

Tell the class about the tour organizers' plans to test their tour. Have students look at the table (time, distance) data collected on Day 1.

Review the decisions students will need to make to make a graph of the data. Read Problem 1.3 with students. Have students work in small groups or pairs on the problem.

Materials
- Transparency 1.3A

Explore

As you visit groups, determine who is still having difficulties with graphing.

- *What times of day do you think are represented by 0 hours, 0.5 hours, and so on?*
- *Do you think the students stopped for lunch? When did they stop?*
- *How is the lunch stop shown in the table and graph?*
- *Do you think they got tired as the day progressed? Explain.*

Summarize

Display Transparency 1.3B. Have students discuss the scales, axis labels, and titles and the importance of these elements to the graph.

- *Which variable is displayed on the x-axis?* (time) *Why?*
- *What is the least value on the x-axis? What is the greatest value on the x-axis?*
- *Why is it reasonable to have the size of the interval for the x-axis be 0.5 hours?*
- *Which variable is displayed on the y-axis?*
- *What is the least value on the y-axis? What is the greatest value on the y-axis?*
- *What is the size of the interval for the y-axis on this graph? Did anyone use an interval other than 5 miles for the y-axis?*

Ask students what it means if two points are connected with a line segment and in what types of situations connecting plotted points makes sense.

Spend time discussing rate of change and the answers to part (3) of Question B. These are important ideas.

Materials
- Transparencies 1.3B and 1.3C
- Student notebooks

continued on next page

Have some students share the descriptions they wrote for Question C. After each description, ask students to identify patterns of change, and give possible reasons for the changes. Make sure students use the word *variable* in the conversation.

Question D requires students to think about the strengths and weaknesses of the table and graph representations. Have students share their ideas.

ACE Assignment Guide for Problem 1.3

Core 4, 5, 26
Other unassigned choices from earlier problems

Adapted For suggestions about adapting ACE exercises, see the *CMP Special Needs Handbook.*

Answers to Problem 1.3

A.

Atlantic City to Cape May

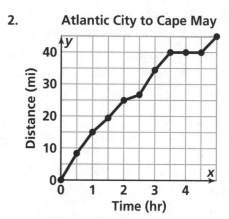

B. 1. (1, 15). This point tells us that after 1 hour the cyclists have gone 15 miles.

2.

Atlantic City to Cape May

Find the location of 0.75 on the *x*-axis, midway between 0.5 and 1. Draw a perpendicular line straight up until it intersects the graph. Then draw a perpendicular line from this point to the *y*-axis. The estimated distance is shown on the *y*-axis at the point of intersection, which is about 11.5 miles.

3. a. ii   **b.** iv   **c.** iii   **d.** i

C. Possible answers: They traveled a total of 45 miles in 5 hours. The riders made the most progress between 0 hours and 0.5 hours, traveling 8 miles. They made the least progress from 3.5 hours to 4.5 hours, when they did not go anywhere. We do not know what time it was when they began riding, but they covered more ground during their first 2.5 hours than their last 2.5 hours—27 miles compared with 18 miles.

D. Students who choose the table may say that it gives exact distances for a given times. Students who choose the graph may say that it shows the "picture" of all the data for the day. It is easy to see from the graph when the change in distance is great, when it is small, and when it does not change.

Day 2: Lewes to Chincoteague Island

Goals

- Identify patterns and relationships between variables using information in a graph

- Create a table from data in a coordinate graph

- Compare patterns of change in a table and graph

This problem gives the data for Day 2 of the bike tour in the form of a graph. The questions ask students to interpret the graph and to create a data table based on the graph.

Launch 1.4

Describe Day 2 to your students. Have students examine the graph. Call attention to the change in distance between 2.5 and 3 hours.

Suggested Questions Ask students:

- *What does the decrease mean?* (The riders backtracked—making them closer to Lewes.)

Students may need to be reminded that this graph shows the distance from Lewes rather than the total distance traveled.

- *Explain what might have happened to make the riders reduce their distance from Lewes.* (Construction caused a detour, someone lost something and they all went back to search for it, they missed a turn and had to turn around, and so on.)

Briefly explain Problem 1.4 to your students and then turn them loose to work individually or in pairs. Be sure that each person makes his or her own table from the graph and records his or her answers.

Explore 1.4

Suggested Questions If students are having difficulty making a table, ask:

- *What two variables are represented in the graph?*

- *What role do variables play when making a table?* (If students don't know, have them look at the table given for Problem 1.3 and the graph they constructed for that problem.)

- *What does this tell you about the labels for your table?*

- *What does this point on the graph tell you? What does the x-coordinate of the point represent? What does the y-coordinate represent?*

- *Show how you would enter the information about the point we looked at into the table.*

Students who are having difficulty identifying and interpreting points from the graph may find it helpful to review the tables and graphs in Problem 1.3.

You may wish to ask students who finish early to make their table on a transparency to share during the summary.

Summarize 1.4

Question A raises the issue of connecting points on a graph—an idea introduced in Problem 1.3. Throughout this unit, students are asked to think about whether connecting the points on a graph makes sense. In this case, it does because the distance changes continuously over the 7.5-hour period.

Students should understand that connecting points can help them see patterns of change more easily and make predictions or estimates about values between plotted points. However, they should also recognize that, connecting points with straight segments shows a constant rate of change between points, which may not accurately reflect the real situation.

Suggested Questions

- *Does it make sense to connect the points in this graph?* (If they say no, ask if that means the riders make progress between points. You want them to realize that time passes and distance may be covered between points, so it makes sense to connect them.)

• *So, if we agree to connect the points, how might you connect them?* (They may have various ideas.) *What would it mean if the points were connected with straight line segments?* (The riders were going at a constant speed during each half-hour interval.)

For Question B, have a couple of students share their tables with the class. If some students are still struggling with reading data points and making a table, ask presenters to explain how they made their table. If all students were able to make a table with no problems, move on. Have students relate the values in a table to the coordinates of a point, and then have them use the coordinates of the point to show these values represent horizontal and vertical distances from the origin to the point.

For Question C students have to speculate on why the backtracking shown in the graph may have occurred. Some students may suggest that someone left something behind when they stopped, and so the riders had to go back to get it.

In Question D, the least progress was made between hours 2.5 and 3 when they went off course for about 8 miles. The most progress was made between hours 4 and 4.5 when they traveled about 12 miles.

In Question E, students choose the display of information they prefer and explain why. The class conversation should include a discussion of the strengths and weaknesses of each representation. (The graph gives a quick visual overview of the day at a glance. The table gives a numerical list of the total miles away from Lewes by a certain time in a very convenient form. However, both the graph and the table give only estimates.)

Question F is a computation problem and can be asked after going over the other parts of the problem. Make sure someone explains why the total distance traveled for the day is not 81 miles (or 82 miles) but is the sum of 81 + 8 + 8, or 97 miles.

1.4 ▶ Day 2: Lewes to Chincoteague Island

Mathematical Goals

- Identify patterns and relationships between variables using information in a graph
- Create a table from data in a coordinate graph
- Compare patterns of change in a table and graph

Launch

Describe Day 2 to your students, and have students discuss the graph. Call attention to the change in distance between 2.5 and 3 hours and ask students what the decrease means.

Tell the class about Problem 1.4. Then have them work individually or in pairs.

Materials
- Transparency 1.4

Explore

If students are having difficulty making a table, ask

- *Which two variables are being represented on the graph?*
- *What role do variables play when making a table? What does this tell you about the labels for your table?*
- *What does this point on the graph tell you? What does the x-coordinate of the point represent? What does the y-coordinate represent?*
- *Show how you would enter the point we looked at into the table.*

You may wish to ask students who finish early to make their table on a transparency to share during the summary.

Materials
- Blank transparencies

Summarize

Discuss Question A, which asks about connecting points on the graph.

- *Does it make sense to connect the points in this graph?*
- *So, if we agree to connect the points, how might you connect them? What would it mean if the points were connected with straight line segments?*

For Question B, have a couple of students share their table with the class. If some students are struggling, ask presenters to explain how they created their tables.

For Question C, ask students to share their ideas about why the backtracking shown in the graph may have occurred.

The discussion of Question E should include the strengths and weaknesses of each form of each representation (graph and table).

For Question F, make sure a student explains why the total distance is 97 miles, and not 81 or 82.

Materials
- Student notebooks

ACE Assignment Guide
for Problem 1.4

Core 6–9, 27
Other *Connections* 21–24; *Extensions* 28;
unassigned choices from earlier problems

Adapted For suggestions about adapting
ACE exercises, see the *CMP Special Needs
Handbook.*
Connecting to Prior Units 21–24: *Data About Us*

Answers to Problem 1.4

A. Answers will vary. Connecting points can help
us see patterns of change in the data.
However, a straight segment would imply that
the riders were traveling at a constant speed
between points, which may not be true.

B. Although the format of the students' tables
may vary, the information should be roughly
the same as that shown here. Values will vary
slightly depending on students' estimates of
the coordinates of the points. (Figure 1)

C. Possible answer: Between hours 2 and 4, the
riders needed to make a detour that brought
them closer to Lewes. They may have forgotten
something and had to go back to get it. After
the detour, they continued on to Chincoteague
Island. Between hours 1.5 and 2, the riders
may have taken a rest break to sightsee.

D. Least progress: between hours 2.5 and 3, when
they lost about 8 miles. Most progress:
between hours 4 and 4.5, when they
progressed about 12 miles.

E. Students' preferences and reasons will vary.
The graph gives a quick overview of the day
at a glance, but it is harder to know what the
individual data values are and the actual
amount of change between them. The table
gives the total miles away from Lewes after a
certain time in a convenient and more exact
form, but it is difficult to get a quick overview
of the whole day.

F. Assuming they only backtracked to mile 22,
the total distance traveled for the day is the
distance the riders are from Lewes at the end
of the day plus the distance they traveled when
they had to backtrack: 81 + 8 + 8, or 97 miles.

Figure 1

Time (hr)	0	0.5	1	1.5	2	2.5	3	3.5	4	4.5	5	5.5	6	6.5	7	7.5
Distance (mi)	0	7	13	22	22	30	22	31	36	48	48	56	63	72	74	81

Day 3: Chincoteague Island to Norfolk

Goal

- Interpret narrative notes to make a table and a graph

This problem gives narrative notes about Day 3 of the bike tour. Students must interpret the notes to make a table and a graph. This problem is more open-ended than the previous problems. However, students should be asked to explain or justify the decisions they made in interpreting the notes.

Launch 1.5

Tell your class about Day 3.

Suggested Questions You may wish to help students make sense of the problem by asking the following questions:

- *What are the two variables you will represent in the table and the graph?* (time and distance)

- *What will you use for your time intervals?* (A common suggestion is a half hour because previous problems have given distances for half-hour intervals.)

- *At 0 hours, what is the distance traveled?* (0 miles) *How do you know?* (Because at 0 hours you are just about to start the day's travel and have not gone anywhere yet.)

- *At 7.5 hours what is the distance traveled?* (80 miles) *How do you know?* (The last note states that the total distance traveled for the day, at the end of the 7.5 hours, was 80 miles.)

- *What other data points in the table would be easy to fill in based on the set of notes?* (At approximately noon, or 3.5 hours into the trip, riders had traveled about half the total distance, or 40 miles.)

Encourage students to come up with their own data based on the constraints given in Malcolm and Tony's notes to help them complete the problem.

Have students work Problem 1.5 individually or in pairs. If they work with a partner, make sure each student makes a table and a graph.

Explore 1.5

Because this question is so open-ended, many solutions are possible. You may wish to have students make their final tables and graphs on large sheets of paper. These can be displayed for comparison during the summary. Some students may find it helpful to include the time of day, in addition to the elapsed time, on these representations to assist them in answering the questions.

Be sure students are using all the relevant information given to create their data table and graph. They will probably need to use trial-and-error methods to make their data satisfy all the constraints.

Suggested Questions For students who struggle, you may need to ask questions like the following:

- *How would riding into a strong wind affect the speed the riders could travel?* (It would slow them down.)

- *How would riding with the wind at their backs affect the speed?* (It would help the riders go faster.)

- *Which clues give you information you could use to locate approximate points for your table?* (Various answers, but the first, third, fifth, and sixth clues might be mentioned.)

Summarize 1.5

Have students share their tables and graphs. Ask the class to look over all the displays and check for similarities and differences among them. Ask if anyone's data seem unreasonable and why. Let that student respond, either defending the data or agreeing and changing the values accordingly. The tables and graphs will be different but should share these common characteristics:

- If reported in half-hour intervals, there will be 16 data entries.

- The total distance must be 80 miles.

- The early morning's progress should be slower than the rest of the day because of the wind.

- There are three breaks: at midmorning, at lunch time, and at around 2:00 P.M. (or from hours 5.5–6.0).

- When the riders load their cycles in the van to cross the Chesapeake Bay Bridge and Tunnel, we might assume they will cover a greater distance in a shorter time than when they were pedaling.

Ask two students with different, but correct, graphs to share their answers for Question C. Encourage other students to ask questions so they can understand what assumptions and interpretations the presenters made in constructing their graph.

Questions D and E can be discussed together as both explore constant speed.

Suggested Questions Ask questions such as these:

- *How do you find the average speed?* (Take the total miles and divide by the number of hours. This gives the average speed in miles per hour.)

- *Could you divide the hours by the miles?* (Yes, but this would give you the number of hours per mile which is not the usual way of representing speed.)

- *What does the "average" speed mean?* (The number of miles per hour averaged over the entire trip.)

- *If the riders were able to travel this average speed consistently over the entire route, how long would it take them to reach the destination?* (7.5 hours)

- *What would the graph have looked like if the riders had traveled at this average speed all day?* (It would be a straight line from beginning to end with no change in steepness at any point.)

- *How would it compare to the graph you made based on interpreting the descriptions?* (The graphs we made had changes in steepness between points based on wind conditions and breaks.)

1.5 Day 3: Chincoteague Island to Norfolk

Mathematical Goal

- Interpret narrative notes to make a table and a graph

Launch

Tell your class about Day 3.

- *What are the two variables you will represent in the table and the graph?*
- *What will you use for your time intervals?*
- *At 0 hours, what is the distance traveled? How do you know?*
- *At 7.5 hours what is the distance traveled? How do you know?*
- *What other data points in the table would be easy to fill in based on the set of notes?*

Have students work Problem 1.5 individually or in pairs, but make sure each student makes a graph and table.

Materials
- Transparency 1.5

Explore

Many solutions are possible. You may wish to have students make their final tables and graphs on large sheets of paper. These can be displayed and compared during the summary.

For students who struggle, consider asking:

- *How would riding into a strong wind affect the speed the riders could travel?*
- *How would riding with the wind at their backs affect the speed?*
- *Which clues give you information you could use to locate approximate points for your table?*

Materials
- Large sheets of paper

Summarize

Have students share their tables and graphs. Ask the class to look over all the displays and check for similarities and differences among them.

Ask if anyone's data seem unreasonable and why. Let that student respond, either defending the data or agreeing and changing the values accordingly.

Ask two students with different, but correct, graphs to share their answers for Question C.

Questions D and E can be discussed as a class.

- *How do you find the average speed?*
- *Could you divide the hours by the miles?*
- *What does the "average" speed mean?*

Materials
- Student notebooks

continued on next page

continued

- *If the riders were able to travel this average speed consistently over the entire route, how long would it take them to reach the destination?*

- *What would the graph have looked like if the riders had traveled at this average speed all day?*

- *How would it compare to the graph you made based on interpreting the descriptions?*

ACE Assignment Guide for Problem 1.5

Differentiated Instruction
Solutions for All Learners

Core 10, 12
Other *Applications* 11, *Connections* 25; *Extensions* 29, 30; unassigned choices from earlier problems

Adapted For suggestions about adapting Exercise 10 and other ACE exercises, see the *CMP Special Needs Handbook*.

Answers to Problem 1.5

A. Possible answer: (Figure 2)

B. Possible answer: (Figure 3)

C. Possible answer: I decided to use half-hour intervals because all the tables and graphs in this investigation used that size time interval. Using the information that the trip started at 8:30 a.m. (first note) and that they traveled for 7.5 hours, I filled in the time column of my

table. I also could fill in the distance value to match the last time entry because the last note says they traveled 80 miles. The next note I used was the third one, which stated that the stop for lunch was about an hour and that they had traveled about halfway. I decided that noon was a reasonable time for lunch (3.5 hours into the trip) and 40 would be the travel distance for that time because it is halfway. After that I used notes 1 and 2 to spread out the first 40 miles of the trip and notes 4 and 5 to spread out the last 40 miles of the trip. To make the graph, I put time on the x-axis and distance on the y-axis and plotted the data points from my table.

D. 80 miles ÷ 7.5 hours = $10\frac{2}{3}$ miles per hour

E. The graph would be a straight line from $(0, 0)$ to the point $(7.5, 80)$. This is different from the graph in Question B, in which the steepness changes at various points in the graph as the riders' speed changed.

Figure 2

Time (hr)	0.0	0.5	1.0	1.5	2.0	2.5	3.0	3.5	4.0	4.5	5.0	5.5	6.0	6.5	7.0	7.5
Distance (mi)	0.0	3.0	5.0	8.0	18.0	25.0	33.0	40.0	40.0	40.0	47.0	54.0	54.0	57.0	60.0	80.0

Figure 3

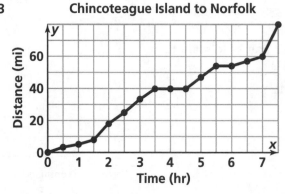

Chincoteague Island to Norfolk

Variables, Tables, and Coordinate Graphs

The bicycle was invented in 1791. People of all ages use bicycles for transportation and sport. Many people spend their vacations taking organized bicycle tours.

Did You Know?

RAGBRAI, which stands for Register's Annual Great Bicycle Ride Across Iowa, is a weeklong cycling tour across the state of Iowa. The event has been held every summer since 1973. Although the tour follows a different route each year, it always begins with as many as 10,000 participants dipping their back bicycle wheels into the Missouri River along Iowa's western border and ends with the riders dipping their front wheels into the Mississippi River on Iowa's eastern border.

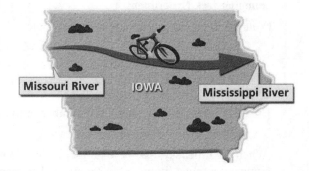

Go Online
PHSchool.com   **For:** Information about RAGBRAI
Web Code: ane-9031

Investigation 1 Variables, Tables, and Coordinate Graphs   **5**

Notes _____

_____

_____

_____

Preparing for a Bicycle Tour

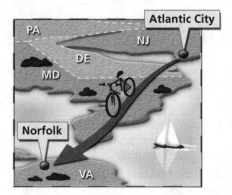

Sidney, Celia, Liz, Malcolm, and Theo decide to operate bicycle tours as a summer business. The five college students choose a route from Atlantic City, New Jersey, to Norfolk, Virginia. The students name their business Ocean Bike Tours.

While planning their bike tour, the students need to determine how far the touring group can ride each day. To figure this out, they take test rides around their hometowns.

Getting Ready for Problem

- How far do you think you could ride in a day?
- How do you think the speed of your ride would change during the course of the day?
- What conditions would affect the speed and distance you could ride?

To accurately answer the questions above, you would need to take a test ride yourself. Instead you can perform an experiment involving jumping jacks. This experiment should give you some idea of the patterns commonly seen in tests of endurance.

Jumping Jack Experiment

You will need a group of at least four people:

- a jumper (to do jumping jacks)
- a timer (to keep track of the time)
- a counter (to count jumping jacks)
- a recorder (to write down the number of jumping jacks)

As a group, decide who will do each task.

When the timer says "go," the jumper begins doing jumping jacks. The jumper continues jumping for 2 minutes. The counter counts the jumping jacks out loud. Every 10 seconds, the timer says "time" and the recorder records the total number of jumping jacks the jumper has done.

6 Variables and Patterns

Notes _____

_____

_____

_____

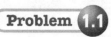

Problem 1.1 Interpreting Tables

A. Do the jumping jack experiment. For each jumper, prepare a table for recording the total number of jumping jacks after every 10 seconds, up to a total time of 2 minutes (120 seconds).

Jumping Jack Experiment

Time (seconds)	0	10	20	30	40	50	60	70	...
Total Number of Jumping Jacks	0	12	32	59	65	75			
Jumping Jack Rate	0	1.2	1.6	1.9	1.6	1.5			

JUMPS/ sec

Use the table of your jumping jack data to answer these questions:

B. How did the jumping jack rates (the number of jumping jacks per second) in your group change as time passed? How is this shown in your tables?

C. What might this pattern suggest about how bike-riding speed would change over a day's time on the bicycle tour?

ACE Homework starts on page 15.

1.2 Making Graphs

In the jumping jack experiment, the number of jumping jacks and the time are variables. A **variable** is a quantity that changes or varies. You recorded data for the experiment variables in a table. Another way to display your data is in a **coordinate graph.** Making a coordinate graph is a way to show the relationships between two variables.

Investigation 1 Variables, Tables, and Coordinate Graphs   **7**

Notes _____
_____
_____
_____

There are four steps to follow when you make a coordinate graph.

Step 1 Identify two variables.

In Problem 1.1, the two variables are *time* and *number of jumping jacks.*

Step 2 Select an axis to represent each variable.

Often, you can assign each variable to an axis by thinking about how the variables are related. If one variable depends on the other, put the dependent variable on the **y-axis** (the vertical axis) and the **independent variable** on the **x-axis** (the horizontal axis). You may have encountered the terms *dependent variable* and *independent variable* in your science classes.

If time is a variable, you usually put it on the *x*-axis. This helps you see the "story" that occurs over time as you read the graph from left to right.

In Problem 1.1, the number of jumping jacks depends on time. So, put number of jumping jacks (the dependent variable) on the *y*-axis and time (the independent variable) on the *x*-axis.

Label your graph so that someone else can see what it represents. You can label the *x*-axis as "Time (seconds)" and the *y*-axis as "Number of Jumping Jacks." You can use these labels to help you choose a title for your graph. You might title this graph, "Jumping Jacks Over Time."

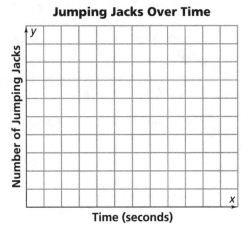

Jumping Jacks Over Time

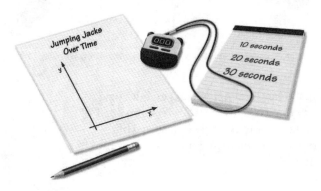

Notes _____

_____

_____

_____

Step 3 Select a **scale** for each axis. For each axis, determine the least and greatest values to show. Then decide how to space the scale marks.

In Problem 1.1, the values for time are between 0 and 120 seconds. On the graph, label the x-axis (time) from 0 to 120. Because you collected data every 10 seconds, label by 10's.

The scale you use on the y-axis (number of jumping jacks) depends on the number of jumping jacks you did. For example, if you did 97 jumping jacks, you could label your scale from 0 to 100. Because it would take a lot of space to label the scale for every jumping jack, you could label by 10's.

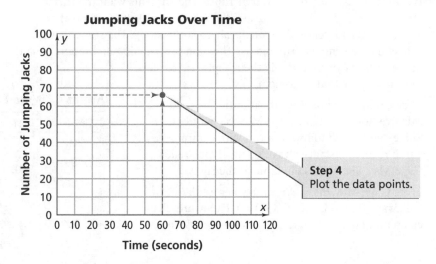

Jumping Jacks Over Time

Step 4
Plot the data points.

Step 4 Plot the data points.

Suppose that at 60 seconds, you had done 66 jumping jacks. To plot this information, start at 60 on the x-axis (time) and follow a line straight up. On the y-axis (number of jumping jacks), start at 66 and follow a line straight across. Make a point where the two lines intersect. You can describe this point with the **coordinate pair** (60, 66). The first number in a coordinate pair is the x-coordinate, and the second number is the y-coordinate.

Problem 1.2 Making Graphs

A. Make a graph of the jumping jack data for one of the jumpers in your group.

B. What does your graph show about the jumping jack rate as time passes? (Another way to say this is, what does your graph show about the **relationship** between the number of jumping jacks and time?)

C. Is the relationship you found between the number of jumping jacks and time easier to see in the table or in the graph? Explain.

ACE Homework starts on page 15.

Investigation 1 Variables, Tables, and Coordinate Graphs   **9**

Notes

Sidney, Liz, Celia, Malcolm, and Theo found they could comfortably ride from 60 to 90 miles in one day. They use these findings, as well as a map and campground information, to plan a three-day tour route. They wonder if steep hills and rough winds coming off the ocean might make the trip too difficult for some riders.

It is time to test the projected tour route. The students want the trip to attract middle school students, so Sidney asks her 13-year-old brother, Tony, and her 14-year-old sister, Sarah, to come along. The students will collect data during the trip and use the data to write detailed reports. Using the reports, they can improve their plans and explain the trip to potential customers.

They begin their bike tour in Atlantic City and ride five hours south to Cape May, New Jersey. Sidney and Sarah follow in a van with camping gear. Sarah records distances traveled until they reach Cape May. She makes the table at the right.

From Cape May, they take a ferry across the Delaware Bay to Lewes (LOO-is), Delaware. They camp that night in a state park along the ocean.

Atlantic City to Cape May

Time (hr)	Distance (mi)
0	0
0.5	8
1.0	15
1.5	19
2.0	25
2.5	27
3.0	34
3.5	40
4.0	40
4.5	40
5.0	45

Problem 1.3 Interpreting Graphs

A. Make a coordinate graph of the time and distance data in Sarah's table. Show time on the *x*-axis.

B. Analyze your graph by answering the following questions:

   1. Give the coordinate pair for the third point on your graph. What information does this point give?

   2. Connecting the points on a graph sometimes helps you see a pattern more clearly. You can connect the points to consider what is happening in the intervals between the points.

     Connect the points on your graph with straight line segments. Use the line segments to estimate the distance traveled after $\frac{3}{4}$ of an hour (0.75 hours).

10 Variables and Patterns

Notes

_____

_____

_____

_____

3. The straight-line segment you drew from (4.5, 40) to (5.0, 45) shows the progress if the riders travel at a steady rate for the entire half hour. The actual pace of the group, and of individual riders, may vary throughout the half hour. These paths show some possible ways the ride may have progressed:

Match each of these connecting paths with the travel notes below.

a. Celia rode slowly at first and gradually increased her speed.

b. Tony and Liz rode quickly and reached the campsite early.

c. Malcolm had to fix a flat tire, so he started late.

d. Theo started off fast. He soon felt tired and slowed down.

C. Sidney wants to describe Day 1 of the tour. Using information from the table or the graph, what can she write about the day's travel? Consider the following questions:

- How far did the group travel? How much time did it take them?

- During which time interval(s) did they go the greatest distance? During which time interval(s) did they go the least distance?

- Did the riders go farther in the first half or the second half of the day's ride?

D. Sidney wants to include either the table or the graph in her report. Which do you think she should include? Why?

ACE Homework starts on page 15.

Notes _____

_____

_____

_____

1.4 Day 2: Lewes to Chincoteague Island

On Day 2, the students leave Lewes, Delaware, and ride through Ocean City, Maryland. They stop for the day on Chincoteague (SHING kuh teeg) Island, which is famous for its annual pony auction.

Did You Know?

Assateague (A suh teeg) Island is home to herds of wild ponies. To survive in a harsh environment of beaches, sand dunes, and marshes, these sturdy ponies eat saltmarsh, seaweed, and even poison ivy!

To keep the population of ponies under control, an auction is held every summer. During the famous "Pony Swim," the ponies that will be sold swim across a quarter mile of water to Chincoteague Island.

Go Online
PHSchool.com
For: Information about the "Pony Swim"
Web Code: ane-9031

Celia collects data along the way and uses it to make the graph below. Her graph shows the distance the riders are from Lewes as the day progresses. This graph is different from the graph made for Problem 1.3, which showed the total distance traveled as Day 1 progressed.

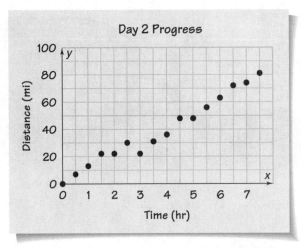

Day 2 Progress

12 Variables and Patterns

Notes _____

_____

_____

_____

Problem 1.4 Reading Data from Graphs

A. Does it make sense to connect the points on this graph? Explain.

B. Make a table of (*time, distance*) data that matches the coordinate pairs of the graph. (You will need to estimate many of the distance values.)

C. What might have happened between hours 2 and 4? What do you think happened between hours 1.5 and 2?

D. During which interval(s) did the riders make the most progress? During which interval(s) did they make the least progress?

E. Which method of displaying the data helps you see the changes better, a table or a graph? Explain.

F. Use the graph to find the total distance the riders travel on Day 2. How did you find your answer?

ACE Homework starts on page 15.

Did You Know?

The Global Positioning System (GPS) is a satellite navigation system funded and operated by the U.S. Department of Defense. However, there are many thousands of civilian users of GPS worldwide. With the use of a portable computer, a Braille keyboard, and a GPS receiver, a blind person is able to get directions.

Go Online
PHSchool.com
For: Information about GPS
Web Code: ane-9031

Investigation 1 Variables, Tables, and Coordinate Graphs   **13**

Notes _____

_____

_____

_____

On Day 3, the group travels from Chincoteague Island to Norfolk, Virginia. Malcolm and Tony ride in the van. They forget to record the distance traveled each half hour, but they do write some notes about the trip.

- We started at 8:30 A.M. and rode into a strong wind until our midmorning break.

- About midmorning, the wind shifted to our backs.

- We stopped for lunch at a barbeque stand and rested for about an hour. By this time, we had traveled about halfway to Norfolk.

- Around 2:00 P.M., we stopped for a brief swim in the ocean.

- Around 3:30 P.M., we reached the north end of the Chesapeake Bay Bridge and Tunnel. We stopped for a few minutes to watch the ships passing. Because riding bikes on the bridge is not allowed, we put the bikes in the van and drove across.

- We took 7.5 hours to complete today's 80-mile trip.

Problem 1.5 **Finding Average Speed**

A. Make a table of (*time, distance*) data that reasonably fits the information in Malcolm and Tony's notes.

B. Sketch a coordinate graph that shows the same information.

C. Explain how you used each of the six notes to make your table and graph.

D. The riders traveled 80 miles in 7.5 hours. Suppose they had traveled at a constant speed for the entire trip. This constant speed would be the same as the *average speed* of the real trip. What was the average speed for this trip?

E. Suppose you made a (*time, distance*) graph for a rider who made the entire 7.5-hour trip traveling at the average speed you found in Question D. What would the graph look like? How would it compare with the graph you made in Question B?

ACE **Homework starts on page 15.**

14 Variables and Patterns

Notes _____

_____

_____

_____

Applications

1. A convenience store has been keeping track of its popcorn sales.

Popcorn Sales

Time	Total Bags Sold
6:00 A.M.	0
7:00 A.M.	3
8:00 A.M.	15
9:00 A.M.	20
10:00 A.M.	26
11:00 A.M.	30
noon	45
1:00 P.M.	58
2:00 P.M.	58
3:00 P.M.	62
4:00 P.M.	74
5:00 P.M.	83
6:00 P.M.	88
7:00 P.M.	92

a. Make a coordinate graph of the data in the table above. Which variable did you put on the *x*-axis? Why?

b. Describe how the number of bags of popcorn sold changed during the day.

c. During which hour did the store sell the most popcorn? During which hour did it sell the least popcorn?

For: Climbing Monkeys
Activity
Visit: PHSchool.com
Web Code: and-1101

Investigation 1 Variables, Tables, and Coordinate Graphs   **15**

Notes _____

_____

_____

_____

2. At the right is a graph of jumping jack data. (On the x-axis, 20 means the interval from 0 seconds to 20 seconds, 40 means the interval 20 seconds to 40 seconds, and so on.)

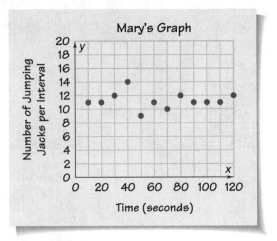

   a. What does the graph tell you about Mary's experiment?

   b. How is this graph different from the graph you made in Problem 1.2?

   c. What total number of jumping jacks did Mary do?

3. After doing the jumping jack experiment, Andrea and Ken compare their graphs. Because the points on his graph are higher, Ken said he did more jumping jacks in the 120 seconds than Andrea did. Do you agree? Explain.

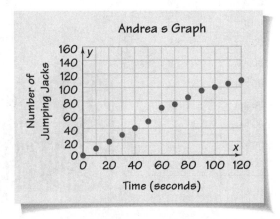

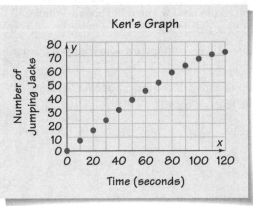

Notes _____

_____

_____

_____

4. Katrina's parents kept this record of her growth from her birth until her 18th birthday.

Katrina's Height

Age (yr)	Height (in.)
birth	20
1	29
2	33.5
3	37
4	39.5
5	42
6	45.5
7	47
8	49
9	52
10	54
11	56.5
12	59
13	61
14	64
15	64
16	64
17	64.5
18	64.5

a. Make a coordinate graph of Katrina's height data.

b. During which time interval(s) did Katrina have her greatest "growth spurt"?

c. During which time interval(s) did Katrina's height change the least?

d. Would it make sense to connect the points on the graph? Why or why not?

e. Is it easier to use the table or the graph to answer parts (b) and (c)? Explain.

Notes _____

_____

_____

_____

5. Below is a chart of the water depth in a harbor during a typical 24-hour day. The water level rises and falls with the tides.

Effect of the Tide on Water Depth

Hours Since Midnight	0	1	2	3	4	5	6	7	8
Depth (m)	10.1	10.6	11.5	13.2	14.5	15.5	16.2	15.4	14.6

Hours Since Midnight	9	10	11	12	13	14	15	16
Depth (m)	12.9	11.4	10.3	10.0	10.4	11.4	13.1	14.5

Hours Since Midnight	17	18	19	20	21	22	23	24
Depth (m)	15.4	16.0	15.6	14.3	13.0	11.6	10.7	10.2

a. At what time is the water the deepest? Find the depth at that time.

b. At what time is the water the shallowest? Find the depth at that time.

c. During what time interval does the depth change most rapidly?

d. Make a coordinate graph of the data. Describe the overall pattern you see.

e. How did you determine what scale to use for your graph? Do you think everyone in your class used the same scale?

Notes

6. Three students made graphs of the population of a town called Huntsville. The break in the *y*-axis in Graphs A and C indicates that there are values missing between 0 and 8.

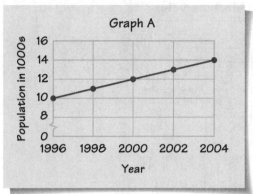

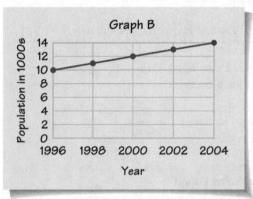

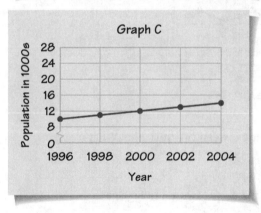

a. Describe the relationship between time and population as shown in each of the graphs.

b. Is it possible that all three graphs correctly represent the population growth in Huntsville? Explain.

Investigation 1 Variables, Tables, and Coordinate Graphs   **19**

Notes _____
_____
_____
_____

7. On the *x*-axis of the graph below, 6 means the time from 5:00 to 6:00, 7 means the time from 6:00 to 7:00, and so on.

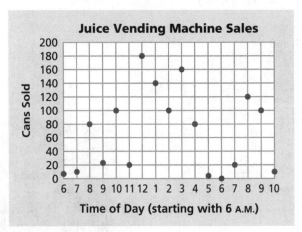

a. The graph shows the relationship between two variables. What are the variables?

b. Describe how the number of cans sold changed during the day. Explain why these changes might have occurred.

8. Here is a graph of temperature data collected on the students' trip from Atlantic City to Lewes.

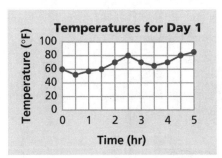

a. This graph shows the relationship between two variables. What are they?

b. Make a table of data from this graph.

c. What is the difference between the day's lowest and highest temperatures?

d. During which time interval(s) did the temperature rise the fastest? During which time interval did it fall the fastest?

20 Variables and Patterns

Notes

_____

_____

_____

_____

e. Is it easier to use the table or the graph to answer part (c)? Why?

f. Is it easier to use the table or the graph to answer part (d)? Why?

g. What information can you get from the lines connecting the points? Do you think it is accurate information? Explain.

9. Here is a graph Celia drew on the bike trip.

   a. What does this graph show?

   b. Is this a reasonable pattern for the speed of a cyclist? Is this a reasonable pattern for the speed of the van? Is this a reasonable pattern for the speed of the wind? Explain each of your conclusions.

Celia's Graph

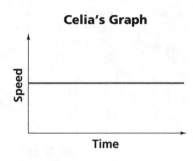

10. Make a table and a graph of (*time*, *temperature*) data that fit the following information about a day on the road:

- We started riding at 8 A.M. The day was quite warm, with dark clouds in the sky.

- About midmorning, the temperature dropped quickly to 63°F, and there was a thunderstorm for about an hour.

- After the storm, the sky cleared and there was a warm breeze.

- As the day went on, the sun steadily warmed the air. When we reached our campground at 4 P.M. it was 89°F.

11. When Ben first started to play the electric guitar, his skill increased quite rapidly. Over time, Ben seemed to improve more slowly.

   a. Sketch a graph to show how Ben's guitar-playing skill progressed over time since he began to play.

   b. Your graph shows the relationship between two variables. What are those variables?

   c. What other variables might affect the rate at which Ben's playing improves?

Investigation 1 Variables, Tables, and Coordinate Graphs   **21**

Notes _____

_____

_____

_____

12. Amanda made the graphs below to show how her level of hunger and her feelings of happiness changed over the course of a day. She forgot to label the graphs.

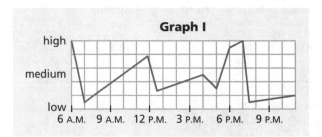

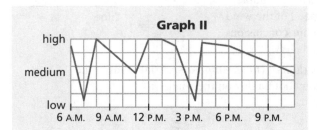

Use the following descriptions to determine which graph shows Amanda's hunger pattern and which graph shows Amanda's happiness. Explain.

Hunger: Amanda woke up really hungry and ate a large breakfast. She was hungry again by lunch, which began at 11:45. After school, she had a snack before basketball practice, but she had a big appetite by the time she got home for dinner. Amanda was full after dinner and did not eat much before she went to bed.

Happiness: Amanda woke up in a good mood, but got mad at her older brother for hogging the bathroom. She talked to a boy she likes on the morning bus. Amanda enjoyed her early classes, but got bored by lunch. At lunch, she had fun with friends. She loved her computer class, which was right after lunch, but she didn't enjoy her other afternoon classes. After school, Amanda had a good time at basketball practice. After dinner, she did homework and chores.

Notes _____

_____

_____

_____

Connections

For Exercises 13–15, order the numbers from least to greatest. Then describe how each number in your ordered list can be obtained from the previous number.

13. 1.75, 0.25, 0.5, 1.5, 2.0, 0.75, 1.25, 1.00

14. $\frac{3}{8}$, 1, $\frac{1}{4}$, $\frac{7}{8}$, $\frac{3}{4}$, $\frac{1}{2}$, $\frac{1}{8}$, $\frac{5}{8}$

15. $\frac{4}{3}$, $\frac{1}{3}$, $\frac{1}{6}$, $\frac{4}{6}$, $\frac{8}{3}$, $\frac{32}{6}$

For: Multiple-Choice Skills Practice
Web Code: ana-1154

16. Draw the next shape in this pattern. Then, make a table of (*number of squares in bottom row, total number of squares*) data for the first five shapes in this pattern.

17. Make a table to show how the total number of cubes in these pyramids changes as the width of the base changes from 3 to 7.

Notes _____

_____

_____

_____

(23) 36

18. Multiple Choice Suppose you know that there are five blocks in a bag, and one of these is marked "winner."

You reach into the bag and choose one block at random. What is the probability you will choose the "winner"?

A. $\frac{1}{5}$ **B.** $\frac{1}{4}$ **C.** $\frac{1}{2}$ **D.** None of these

19. a. Suppose you replace the block you chose in Exercise 18 *and* add another "winner" block. Now there are six blocks in the bag. What is the probability of choosing a "winner" if you choose one block at random?

   b. How does your probability of choosing a "winner" change for every extra "winner" block you add to the bag? Use a table or graph to explain your answer.

20. Suppose you toss a 6-sided die twice to make the coordinate pair (*roll 1, roll 2*). You will win a prize if the result is (2, 2), (4, 4), or (6, 6). What is the probability you will win a prize?

Homework Help Online
PHSchool.com
For: Help with Exercise 20
Web Code: ane-1120

21. The directors of Ocean Bike Tours want to compare their plans with other bicycle tour companies. The bike tour they are planning takes three days, and they wonder if this might be too short. Malcolm called 18 different companies and asked, "How many days is your most popular bike trip?" Here are the answers he received:

   3, 6, 7, 5, 10, 7, 4, 2, 3, 3, 5, 14, 5, 7, 12, 4, 3, 6

Make a line plot of the data.

22. Multiple Choice What is the median of the data in Exercise 21?

   F. 3   **G.** 5   **H.** 6   **J.** 14

24 Variables and Patterns

Notes _____

_____

_____

_____

23. On the basis of the information in Exercises 21 and 22, should Ocean Bike Tours change the length of the three-day trip? Explain.

24. The graph below shows the results of a survey of people over age 25 who had completed different levels of education.

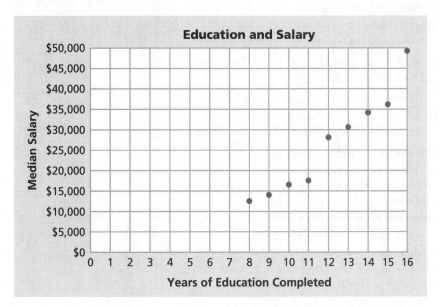

Education and Salary

a. Make a table that shows the information in the graph.

b. After how many years of education do salaries take a big jump? Why do you think this happens?

c. Do you find it easier to answer part (b) by looking at the graph or at your table? Explain.

25. Think of something in your life that varies with time, and make a graph to show how it might change as time passes. Some possibilities are the length of your hair, your height, your moods, or your feelings toward your friends.

Investigation 1 Variables, Tables, and Coordinate Graphs **25**

Notes _____

_____

_____

_____

Extensions

26. The number of hours of daylight in a day changes throughout the year. We say that the days are "shorter" in winter and "longer" in summer. The table shows the number of daylight hours in Chicago, Illinois, on a typical day during each month of the year (January is month 1, and so on).

a. Describe any relationships you see between the two variables.

b. On a grid, sketch a coordinate graph of the data. Put months on the *x*-axis and daylight hours on the *y*-axis. What patterns do you see?

c. The seasons in the southern hemisphere are the opposite of the seasons in the northern hemisphere. When it is summer in North America, it is winter in Australia. Chicago is about the same distance north of the equator as Melbourne, Australia, is south of the equator. Sketch a graph showing the relationship you would expect to find between the month and the hours of daylight in Melbourne.

Daylight Hours

Month	Daylight Hours
1	10.0
2	10.2
3	11.7
4	13.1
5	14.3
6	15.0
7	14.5
8	13.8
9	12.5
10	11.0
11	10.5
12	10.0

d. Put the (*month*, *daylight*) values from your graph in part (c) into a table.

26 Variables and Patterns

Notes _____

_____

_____

_____

27. Some students did a jumping jack experiment. They reported their data in the graph below.

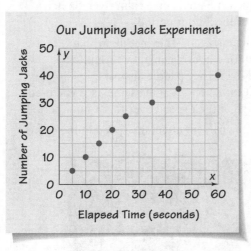

a. According to the graph, how many jumping jacks did the jumper make by the end of 10 seconds? By the end of 20 seconds? By the end of 60 seconds?

b. Give the elapsed time and number of jumping jacks for two other points on the graph.

c. What estimate would make sense for the number of jumping jacks in 30 seconds? The number in 40 seconds? In 50 seconds?

d. What does the overall pattern in the graph show about the rate at which the test jumper completed jumping jacks?

e. Suppose you connected the first and last data points with a straight line segment. Would this line show the overall pattern? Explain.

28. a. A school booster club sells sweatshirts. Which, if any, of the graphs describes the relationship you expect between the price charged for each sweatshirt and the profit? Explain your choice, or draw a new graph you think better describes this relationship.

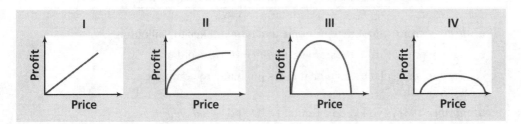

b. What variables might affect the club's profits?

Investigation 1 Variables, Tables, and Coordinate Graphs   **27**

Notes _____

_____

_____

_____

29. Chelsea and Nicole can paddle a canoe at a steady rate of 5 miles per hour.

   a. On Saturday, they paddle for 3 hours on a calm river. Sketch a graph of their speed over the 3-hour period.

   b. On Sunday, they go canoeing again. They paddle with a 2-mile-per-hour current for 1 hour. Then, they turn into a tributary that feeds the river. They paddle against a 2-mile-per-hour current for 2 hours. On the same axes you used in part (a), sketch a graph of their speed over this 3-hour period.

   c. How does the speed of the current affect the speed of the canoe?

30. In parts (a)–(e) below, how does the value of one variable change as the value of the other changes? Estimate pairs of values that show the pattern of change you would expect. Record your estimates in a table with at least five data points.

   Sample *hours* of television you watch in a week and your school *grade-point average*

   As television time increases, I expect my grade-point average to decrease.

TV Time (hours per week)	0	5	10	15	20
Grade Point Average	3.5	3.25	3.0	2.75	2.5

   a. *distance* from school to your home and *time* it takes to walk home

   b. *price* of popcorn at a theater and *number of bags* sold

   c. *speed* of an airplane and *time* it takes the plane to complete a 500-mile trip

   d. *number of days* you keep a rented DVD and *rental charge*

   e. *length* of a long-distance telephone call in minutes and *cost* of the call

28   Variables and Patterns

Notes _____

_____

_____

_____

Mathematical Reflections 1

The problems in this investigation asked you to think about variables and the patterns relating the values of variables. You made tables and graphs to show how different variables are related. The following questions will help you summarize what you have learned.

Think about your answers to these questions. Discuss your ideas with other students and your teacher. Then write a summary of your findings in your notebook.

1. Describe the steps you would take in making a graph to show the relationship between two related variables.

2. How do you decide which variable should be on the *x*-axis and which should be on the *y*-axis?

3. **a.** What are the advantages and disadvantages of representing a relationship between variables in a table?

   b. What are the advantages and disadvantages of representing a relationship between variables in a graph?

   c. What are the advantages and disadvantages of describing a relationship between variables in a written report?

Notes _____

_____

_____

_____

Investigation 1

ACE Assignment Choices

Differentiated Instruction
Solutions for All Learners

Problem 1.1
Core None
Other *Connections* 13–17

Problem 1.2
Core 1–3
Other *Connections* 18–20; unassigned choices from earlier problems

Problem 1.3
Core 4, 5, 26
Other unassigned choices from earlier problems

Problem 1.4
Core 6–9, 27
Other *Connections* 21–24; *Extensions* 28; unassigned choices from earlier problems

Problem 1.5
Core 10, 12
Other *Applications* 11, *Connections* 25; *Extensions* 29, 30; unassigned choices from earlier problems

Adapted For suggestions about adapting Exercise 10 and other ACE exercises, see the CMP *Special Needs Handbook*.
Connecting to Prior Units 13–15: *Bits and Pieces I*; 18–20: *How Likely Is It?*; 21–24: *Data About Us*

Applications

1. a. Time is on the *x*-axis because the number of bags sold depends on the time.

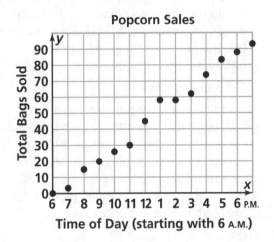

Popcorn Sales

b. Answers will vary. It is important to give students examples of complete and thoughtful responses early in this unit so they have a sense of what is expected. Possible response: Very few bags were sold before 7:00 A.M., perhaps because most people do not eat popcorn so early in the morning. The number jumped by 12 bags between 7:00 A.M. and 8:00 A.M., when people may have stopped for a snack on their way to work or school. The number went up by about 5 bags an hour between 8:00 A.M. and 11:00 A.M. Sales rose by 15 bags between 11:00 A.M. until noon and by 13 bags from noon to 1:00 P.M, when people may have been buying lunch. No popcorn was sold from 1:00 P.M. to 2:00 P.M., and only 4 bags were sold between 2:00 P.M. and 3:00 P.M. Then, the number jumps again by 12 bags from 3:00 P.M. to 4:00 P.M. Maybe people were buying a midafternoon snack. During the next 3 hours, between 4:00 P.M. and 7:00 P.M., the number sold drops from 9 bags to 5 bags to 4 bags. Dinner time is probably the cause of this decrease in sales.

c. 11 A.M. to noon; 1 P.M. to 2 P.M.

Investigation 1 Variable, Tables, and Coordinate Graphs **37**

2. a. Possible answer: The graph shows that Mary was timed for 120 seconds. It shows the number of jumping jacks she did in each 10-second increment of the 120-second time period.

b. The graph from Problem 1.2 showed the *total* number of jumping jacks so far at the end of each 10-second interval. Each point on that graph is higher than the one before because the total number increased with each interval, even when the number done *within* each interval decreased. In Mary's graph, the points go up and down because the number of jumping jacks in some intervals is less than in others.

c. 135 jumping jacks

3. Ken did not do more jumping jacks in 120 seconds. Ken's points are higher because the scales on the two graphs are different. The y-axis on Andrea's graph goes to 160, while the y-axis on Ken's graph goes only to 80. Andrea did about 110 jumping jacks in 120 seconds while Ken did only about 72.

4. a. (Figure 4)

b. between birth and age 1 (9 inches)

c. from age 14 to 16 and from age 17 to 18

d. It makes sense to connect the points because growth occurs between birthdays. (The question of how these points should be connected, by line segments or a curve, is another point of discussion.)

e. Answers will vary. The exact change in height is easier to read from the table. However, students may argue that the graph provides a better overall picture.

5. a. 6 hours after midnight, or 6:00 A.M.; 16.2 m

b. noon; 10.0 m.

c. The water depth changes most rapidly—by 1.7 meters—from 2 to 3 (2 A.M.–3 A.M.), from 8 to 9 (8 A.M.–9 A.M.), and from 14 to 15 (2 P.M.–3 P.M.).

d. (Figure 5) The graph has two humps. It looks symmetric, so that if it were flipped over x = 12 (hour 12), the two parts would align. The graph rises until hour 6, falls until hour 12, and rises again to hour 18, and then falls again.

Figure 4

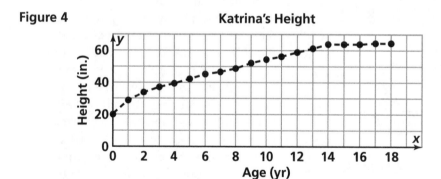

Katrina's Height

Figure 5

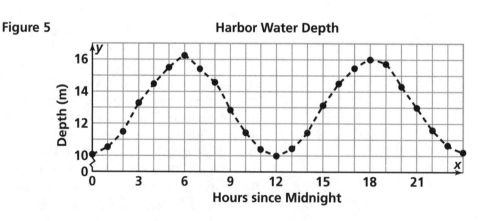

Harbor Water Depth

e. Possible answer: I used 1-hour intervals on the x-axis because that was the time interval in the table. I used 2-meter intervals on the y-axis because it allowed all the data to be graphed on my grid paper. (Not all students will use this scale.)

6. a. In all three graphs the population increases at a steady rate over time (by about 500 people per year).

b. Yes. All three graphs represent the same data. However, the y-axis scales of the graphs are different, giving different impressions of how fast the growth was.

7. a. The two variables are time of day and the number of cans sold each hour.

b. (NOTE: Students may be confused because this is not a cumulative graph. Unlike their graphs showing the jumping jack data, each point in this graph tells how many cans were sold during the one hour preceding that time.) Possible answer: Very few cans were sold before 7:00 A.M., probably because not many people were at school so early. The number jumps to 80 cans at 8:00 A.M. People may have bought juice when they arrived at school. The number drops at 9:00 A.M., when people may have been in class. The number jumps to about 100 cans by 10:00 A.M., when people may have taken a mid-morning break. The number drops to around 20 cans at 11:00 A.M. At noon it jumps to about 180 cans, when some people may have bought juice to go with their lunches. The number goes down again; at 2:00 P.M. about 100 cans were sold. Then the number jumps to about 160 cans at 3:00 P.M., when classes may have been over. The number of cans sold decreases until 6:00 P.M., when no cans were sold. Perhaps most people had already left the school. The number peaks again at 8:00 P.M. when about 120 cans were sold and drops off again until 10:00 P.M. when only about 10 cans were sold. Maybe there was some after-school activity that brought people to school at 8:00 P.M. and then the building closed at 10:00 P.M.

8. a. The variables are time (in hours) and temperature (in degrees Fahrenheit).

b. Values may vary slightly.

Temperatures for Day 1

Time (hr)	Temperature (°F)
0	60
0.5	52
1	57
1.5	60
2	70
2.5	80
3	70
3.5	65
4	70
4.5	80
5	85

c. Possible answer: The high temperature was around 85°F and the low temperature was around 52°F, so the difference is 85 – 52, or 33°F. (Any answer between 31°F and 36°F is acceptable.)

d. The temperature rose fastest between hours 1.5 and 2, 2 and 2.5, and 4 and 4.5. It fell the fastest between hours 2.5 and 3.

e. Answers will vary, but generally it is easier to find the exact size of an increase or decrease using a table.

f. Answers will vary, but generally it is easier to use a graph to find the interval of greatest change because exact calculations do not need to be made.

g. Connecting the points shows the temperature changing at a steady rate between half-hour marks. It makes sense to connect the points because time is a continuous variable, so we will have temperature after 15 minutes, after 37 minutes, and so on. The information may not be completely accurate because the temperature may not have changed at a constant rate. However, it is useful for making estimates.

9. a. A constant speed over a period of time

b. Possible answer: The graph is not reasonable for a cyclist or for the wind under normal conditions. A rider's speed can be affected by fatigue or environmental factors such as temperature, wind speed or direction, and terrain. A van could travel close to a constant speed on a flat surface. The wind usually comes in gusts. It does not seem that it would remain constant over a long period of time. However, one thoughtful student answered: "We don't know what the scale is. So if a small amount of space on the *y*-axis means millions and millions, then this graph is possible for the rider, the van, or the wind because their small amount of speeding up and slowing down wouldn't show up on the graph."

10. Answers will vary, but the graph and the table should show that it was warm at 8 A.M. (at time = 0 hr). Then, the temperature decreased rapidly to 63°F by midmorning and stayed constant for about an hour. After this, the temperature increased until it reached 89°F at 4 P.M.

A Day on the Road

Time (hr)	Temperature (°F)
0	76
1	77
2	63
3	63
4	78
5	80
6	83
7	86
8	89

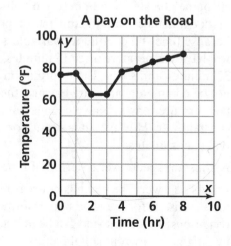

A Day on the Road

11. **a.** A possible graph is shown.

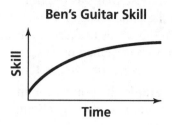

Ben's Guitar Skill

b. The variables are time and skill.

c. Possible answer: hours of practice and the frequency of his lessons

12. Graph I shows Amanda's hunger and Graph II shows her happiness. The increases are quite gradual with hunger and the decreases are rather sudden when Amanda eats. The graph for Amanda's happiness shows that she can stay at the same level of happiness for a while, such as when she is having fun at basketball practice from 4 to 6.

Connections

13. 0.25, 0.5, 0.75, 1.00, 1.25, 1.5, 1.75, 2.0; add 0.25

14. $\frac{1}{8}, \frac{1}{4}, \frac{3}{8}, \frac{1}{2}, \frac{5}{8}, \frac{3}{4}, \frac{7}{8}, 1$; add $\frac{1}{8}$.

15. $\frac{1}{6}, \frac{1}{3}, \frac{4}{6}, \frac{4}{3}, \frac{8}{3}, \frac{32}{6}$; multiply by 2

16.

Number of Squares in Bottom Row	1	2	3	4	5
Total Number of Squares	1	3	6	10	15

17.

Width of Base	3	5	7
Total Number of Cubes	10	35	84

18. A

19. **a.** 2 out of 6, or $\frac{2}{6}$ (or 1 out of 3, or $\frac{1}{3}$)

b. Your probability of winning increases each time you add another winner block. If you have only 1 winner block, your probability of winning is $\frac{1}{5}$. However, if you have 6 winner blocks (10 blocks total), your probability of winning is $\frac{3}{5}$.

Number of Winners	1	2	3	4	5	6
Total Number of Blocks	5	6	7	8	9	10
Probability of Winning	$\frac{1}{5}$	$\frac{1}{3}$	$\frac{3}{7}$	$\frac{1}{2}$	$\frac{5}{9}$	$\frac{3}{5}$

20. 3 out of 36 $(\frac{3}{36})$, or 1 out of 12 $(\frac{1}{12})$

21.

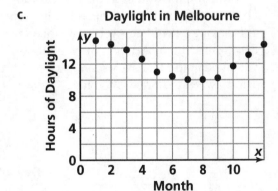

Length of Bike Tours

Number of Days

22. G

23. Answers will vary. Some students may note that the 3-day tour is the most preferred length (that is, 3 days is the mode) and surmise that a 3-day trip is the best option. However, other students may observe that half of the most popular tours are shorter than 5 days (using the median), and half are longer than 5 days, so a 5-day tour is the average length and would be a popular option.

24. **a.** (Figure 6)

b. The greatest increases occur after 12 and 16 years of education. This is probably because a diploma qualifies a person for higher-paying jobs. (You may want to point out to students that these are not starting salaries. Some of these people have been in their field for a number of years. The participants of this study are people over 25.)

c. Answers will vary. It is often easier to see changes, or jumps, in a graph, but it is easier to use a table to find the exact amount of those changes. As the months increase by 1, the daylight hours increase until month 6 and then decrease.

25. Answers will vary.

Extensions

26. **a.** Possible answer: The hours of daylight are least in Jan. and Dec. They are greatest in Jun. The hours of light change most rapidly (by 1.5 hr) from Feb. to Mar. and Sep. to Oct.

b.

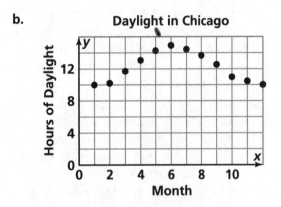

Daylight in Chicago

Possible answer: The number of hours of light increases slowly from Jan. to Jun. and reaches a peak at Jun. It decreases slowly from Jun. to Dec.

c.

Daylight in Melbourne

Figure 6

Years of Education	8	9	10	11	12	13	14	15	16
Median Salary	$12,500	$14,000	$16,500	$17,500	$28,000	$30,500	$34,000	$36,000	$49,000

d. (Figure 7)

27. a. 10 jumping jacks; 20 jumping jacks; 40 jumping jacks

b. Answers will vary.

c. At the end of 30 seconds, the jumper would have done between 25 and 30 jumping jacks. At the end of 40 seconds, the jumper would have done between 30 and 35 jumping jacks. At the end of 50 seconds, the jumper would have done between 35 and 40 jumping jacks.

d. There was a constant increase in the number of jumping jacks for the first 25 seconds. Then, the jumping jack rate started to decrease.

e. It represents the overall trend that as the number of seconds increases, the number of jumping jacks increases. However, it does not show specific details, such as the rate of increase slowing down a bit.

28. a. Answers will vary. Students might make a reasonable argument for any of the graphs. Yet, some graphs seem to be better than others. The following arguments assume that the intersection of the x- and y-axes is point $(0, 0)$ on all graphs. Unlike graph i, graphs ii, iii, and iv represent the idea that profit will not go up indefinitely. When you raise the price too high, some customers will stop buying. Graphs iii and iv show that there is a price that results in the maximum profit. Graph iv is a better representation because graph iii shows the unlikely event of making a profit at a very low price for each shirt. Students might draw a more detailed graph that shows a negative profit (loss) when the price is too low.

b. Possible answers: Selling price, price the club must pay for the sweatshirts, the location and times the booster club chooses for selling sweatshirts, and customer demand (which might depend on other variables such as income and weather).

29. a–b.

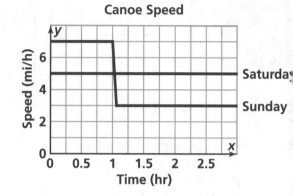

Canoe Speed

c. When Chelsea and Nicole are paddling with the current, their relative speed is 5 mph, the speed they can paddle in calm water, plus the speed of the current. When Chelsea and Nicole are paddling against the current, their relative speed is 5 mph minus the speed of the current.

30. Answers will vary. Possible answers:

a. As distance increases, the time increases.

Distance from School to Home (mi)	Time to Walk Home (min)
$\frac{1}{4}$	5
$\frac{1}{2}$	10
$\frac{3}{4}$	15
1	20
$1\frac{1}{2}$	30

Daylight in Melbourne

Figure 7

Month	1	2	3	4	5	6	7	8	9	10	11	12
Daylight Hours	15	14.5	13.8	12.5	11	10.5	10	10	10.2	11.7	13.1	14.3

b. As the price of popcorn goes up, the number of bags sold goes down.

Price of Popcorn at Theater	Number of Bags Sold
$2	50
$4	40
$6	30
$8	20
$10	10

c. As the airplane speed increases, the time to complete the trip decreases.

Speed of Airplane (miles per hour)	Time to Complete 500-Mile Trip
100	5
125	4
150	3.33
175	2.86
200	2.5

d. As the number of days increases, the late fee increases.

Number of Days	Late Fee
1	$2
2	$4
3	$6
4	$8
5	$10

e. As the length of the call goes up, the charge goes up (except on cell phones, or other special plans).

Length (min)	Cost
1	$0.30
5	$1.50
10	$3.00
15	$4.50
20	$6.00

Possible Answers to Mathematical Reflections

1. **Step 1:** Select two variables you want to represent.

   Step 2: Select an axis to represent each variable. Put the independent variable on the *x*-axis (horizontal axis). If time is one of the variables, you should put it on the *x*-axis.

   Step 3: Select a scale for each axis. For each axis, you need to determine the greatest and least values you want to show on your graph and how you want to space the scale marks.

   Step 4: Label your graph so that someone else would know what the graph represents. Give the graph a title.

   Step 5: Plot points on your graph.

2. If time is one of the variables, you should usually put it on the *x*-axis (the horizontal axis). Otherwise, put the independent variable on the *x*-axis and the dependent variable on the *y*-axis.

3. **a.** A table gives values that are easy to read. However, it is often hard to see patterns or trends at a glance without doing some calculations.

   b. A graph offers a visual image from which you can quickly see patterns in the relationship. However, it is often more difficult to read exact values from a graph.

   c. A written report gives information that cannot be contained in a graph or table, such as the reasons a certain section of a trip took longer than another section. However, in a written report it is difficult to notice patterns or trends.

Mathematical and Problem-Solving Goals

- Compare data sets given in tables and graphs
- Use patterns in data to make predictions about values between and beyond given data values
- Make a graph from a table, choosing the variable and scale for each axis
- Use tables and graphs to analyze data and make decisions
- Predict the pattern in the graph of a relationship between variables
- Tell the "story" shown in a graph

Summary of Problems

Problem 2.1 Renting Bicycles

Students compare bike-rental cost for two companies. One company provides a graph of rental costs, and the other provides a table.

Problem 2.2 Finding Customers

Students graph and analyze information from a survey.

Problem 2.3 Interpreting Graphs

Students are given descriptions of pairs of variables. They match each description with the graph that best tells the "story" of the relationship between the variables.

	Suggested Pacing	Materials for Students	Materials for Teachers	ACE Assignments
All	$4\frac{1}{2}$ days	Calculators		
2.1	1 day	Grid paper (optional)	Transparencies 2.1A and 2.1B (optional)	1–4, 15, 16, 20, 21
2.2	$1\frac{1}{2}$ days	Grid paper, transparent grids	Transparency 2.2 (optional)	5–7, 17, 18, 22, 23
2.3	$1\frac{1}{2}$ days		Transparency 2.3A and 2.3B	8–14, 19, 24
MR	$\frac{1}{2}$ day			

2.1 Renting Bicycles

Goals

- Compare data sets given in tables and graphs
- Use patterns in data to make predictions about values between and beyond given data values

The introduction to Investigation 2 moves the conversation about the bicycle tour from time, distance, and speed to money issues. This allows us to move to tables that have a predictable pattern and, in the next investigation, to capture these patterns in equations.

In Problem 2.1, students work with a table representation of one data set and a graphical representation of a different data set. This problem makes the point that data sets presented in different forms are hard to compare. To make comparisons easier, some students may change the form of representation for one of the data sets. Other students will be able to compare the data by thinking of it as coordinate pairs whether it is displayed in a table or a graph. Many put a finger on a row of the table and a finger on the corresponding point of the graph, and then move their fingers from data pair to data pair, making comparisons.

Launch 2.1

Tell the class about the background of this investigation. Make sure students understand the questions being asked, especially the idea of profit (the amount of money left after all the bills have been paid). Encourage students to share their ideas about what should be provided and to estimate the cost of each item. Students should give the reasons they believe certain items should be provided by the tour company. They should consider that each additional item costs money and therefore increases the cost of the trip for the customer. Students can challenge each other's estimated costs if they seem unreasonable.

If your students have limited experiences with the context of the problem, you may wish to bring in brochures of various types of bike tours (check cycle or travel magazines) to let students get a feel for the prices of tours.

Suggested Questions Use the Getting Ready to start students thinking about the costs involved in running the bike tours.

- *With your classmates, make a list of the things the tour operators will have to provide for their customers. Estimate the cost of each item per customer.* (Possible list: Meals: $100 per person; Accommodations (camping): $75 per person; Water: $10 per person; Bike and helmet: $50 per person)

- *How much do you think customers would be willing to pay for the three-day tour?* (Answers will vary.)

- *Based on your estimates of costs and possible income, will the partners earn a profit?* (Answers will vary. Based on the estimates from the first question and an estimate of $350 for the second question, the partners will earn a profit of $115 per person.)

Read the introduction to Problem 2.1 and have students look at the table and graph.

Suggested Questions Ask these questions to be sure that students understand how to read the table and graph:

- *At Rocky's Cycle Center, what is the cost to rent 5 bicycles?* ($400) *What is the cost to rent 25 bicycles?* ($875) *What is the cost to rent 50 bicycles?* ($1200)

- *At Adrian's Bike Shop, what is the cost to rent 5 bicycles?* (Answers will vary. Students will probably estimate between $150 and $180. It is actually $150, but it is not important to find an exact answer at this time.) *What is the cost to rent 25 bicycles?* (about $780) *What is the cost to rent 50 bicycles?* (about $1500)

When your students have an idea of how to read the table and the graph, talk with them about the problem and what they are expected to do. Highlight the main challenge, namely, to figure out which bike company is a better deal. (They will quickly face the dilemma that it depends on the number of customers. Also, students will see that Adrian's charges are easy to predict, while Rocky's are more difficult because the pattern of change is not linear.)

Have students work on the problem individually and then in pairs.

Suggested Questions Some students may need help to recognize that the number of bikes required is an important part of the decision. To help students notice the difference in price between the two companies, prompt them by asking:

- *Which bike shop should they choose if they need bikes for 10 people?*

- *Which bike shop should they choose if they need bikes for all the students in our class?*

- *Which shop should they choose if they need bikes for four classes the size of ours?*

This problem gives you a chance to spot students who are still having difficulty reading values from graphs and help them sort out their difficulties.

Suggested Question When students are challenged to predict values between entries in a table or points on graph, they sometimes guess, rather than using patterns to make reasonable estimates. If this is a sticking point for students, ask:

- *What evidence do you have that your prediction is reasonable?* (Push students to use observed patterns of change in the table and graph to make their predictions.)

Summarize 2.1

Have students share their findings about which bike shop the tour partners should use and explain how they reached their conclusions.

Suggested Questions Ask students:

- *What are the two variables in this problem?* (The number of bikes and the rental fee)

- *Was it difficult to compare the prices of the two companies? Why or why not?* (Most students will say it was difficult because the price information for the two companies is given in different forms, making it difficult to see differences.)

- *How did you use the information in the table and the graph to help you decide which company the partners should rent from?* (Answers will vary. Some students will say they made a table out of the information in the graph or made a graph of the data from the table so they could better see how the two companies' prices compared.)

If no one suggests representing one of the data sets in a different form, make this suggestion yourself. Making a table for Adrian's Bike Shop and graphing the data for Rocky's Cycle Center should both be explored. You can use Transparency 2.1B to graph the data for Rocky's prices on the same graph as the data for Adrian's. Use a different color so the two data sets are easy to distinguish.

Suggested Questions

- *For both stores, how does the total rental fee change as the number of bikes rented increases?* (The total rental fee increases for every additional bike rented.)

- *For Rocky's Cycle Center, how does the cost per bike change as the number of bikes rented increases?* (The cost per bike decreases as the total number of bikes increases. In other words, the more bikes you rent, the cheaper each bike is.)

- *For Adrian's Bike Shop, how does the cost per bike change as the number of bikes rented increases?* (The cost per bike is always the same—$30 per bike—no matter how many bikes you rent.)

- *How can you decide which bike shop to choose?* (It depends on how many bikes you need. Once you determine about how many bikes you need to rent, compare the cost of both shops for the rentals, and select the shop with the lowest cost.)

Students should talk about the number of bikes required for the tour. For 35 or fewer bikes, the better value is at Adrian's Bike Shop. For more than 35 bikes, Rocky's Cycle Center offers the better value.

Continue the conversation by discussing Questions B through E. Question B is subtle. Some students may suggest that the points be connected because there are values between the points. Make sure students understand that these points should not be connected because one can only rent whole bikes. The x-axis could be rescaled to intervals of 1. With this scaling, it is clearer why the points should not be connected.

For Question C, ask students to explain how they arrived at their rental costs for 32 bikes at each company. After a student has given a method, ask the class if the amount seems reasonable and to explain why. Continue this conversation until all different rental amounts and methods for determining rental fees are presented. Note that ome students may think Adrian's charges the ame amount for all bikes from 30 to 34, and then ₜ 35 bikes the prices jump. If students raise this sue, let the class talk about it and even look at ₕis graph for the situation.

Adrian's Bike Shop Weekly Rates

This lets you look at a step function, which ₘany students find interesting (5 bikes may be ₒnsidered a minimum). The students' ₙterpretation is reasonable because many such ₓamples exist in everyday life. For example, the ₒst of postage is a step function.

Part (1) of Question D asks students to describe the pattern of change in the bicycle rentals, while part (2) ask them how to use these patterns to predict values. Help students see that Adrian's Bike Shop's pattern appears to be linear and easy to describe. Rocky's Bike Shop's pattern is not linear, so it is more difficult to predict values between given values. Here look for good estimates and strategies for making sense of the in-between values.

Students may find it more difficult to describe the pattern of change for Rocky's Cycle Center because it does not have the same amount of increase each time. If students cannot describe this, have them graph the data and describe the arrangement of points on the graph. (They lie on a curve.) Discuss whether it is easier or harder to predict beyond the data in this graph. (It is harder, because the rate of increase is not steady.)

Question E asks specifically for students to articulate strategies for finding the cost of renting any number of bikes from each bike shop. This may emerge in the discussion of Question D.

2.1 Renting Bicycles

Mathematical Goals

- Compare data sets given in tables and graphs
- Use patterns in data to make predictions about values between and beyond given data values

Launch

Use the Getting Ready to start students thinking about the costs involved in running the bike tours.

Read the introduction to Problem 2.1.

- *At Rocky's Cycle Center, what is the cost to rent 5 bikes? What is the cost to rent 25 bikes? What is the cost to rent 50 bikes?*
- *At Adrian's Bike Shop, what is the cost to rent 5 bikes? What is the cost to rent 25 bikes? What is the cost to rent 50 bikes?*

After students understand how to read the table and graph, highlight the main challenge, namely, to figure out which company is a better deal.

Have students work individually and then in pairs.

Materials

- Transparencies 2.1A and 2.1B (optional)
- Brochures for bike tours (optional)

Explore

For students who need help recognizing that the number of bikes required is important, consider asking:

- *Which bike shop should they choose if they need bikes for ten people? For all the students in our math class? For four classes the size of ours? Why?*

For students who guess to estimate values between points, ask:

- *What evidence do you have that your prediction is reasonable?*

Materials

- Grid paper (optional)

Summarize

Have students share their findings regarding which bike shop the tour partners should use and explain how they reached their conclusions.

- *What are the two variables in this problem?*
- *Was it difficult to compare the prices of the two companies? Why or why not?*
- *How did you use the information in the table and the graph to help you decide which company the partners should rent from?*

If no one suggests representing one of the data sets in a different form, make this suggestion yourself.

- *For both stores, how does the total rental fee change as the number of bikes rented increases?*
- *For Rocky's Cycle Center, how does the cost per bike change as the number of bikes rented increases? For Adrian's Bike Shop, how does the cost per bike change as the number of bikes rented increases?*

Materials

- Student notebooks

continued on next page

- *How can you decide which bike shop to choose?*

Continue the conversation by discussing Questions B through E. If students have trouble, have them graph the data.

ACE Assignment Guide for Problem 2.1

Differentiated Instruction
Solutions for All Learners

Core 3, 4, 16
Other *Applications* 1, 2; *Connections* 15; *Extensions* 20, 21; unassigned choices from earlier problems

Adapted For suggestions about adapting Exercise 2 and other ACE exercises, see the *CMP Special Needs Handbook.*
Connecting to Prior Units 15, 16: *Covering and Surrounding*

Answers to Problem 2.1

A. For 35 or fewer bikes, the best value is at Adrian's Bike Shop. For more than 35 bikes, it is at Rocky's Cycle Center. If students calculate the exact amounts, assuming that each bike in the table interval rents for the same amount, the cutoff point is 37 bikes. Explanations will vary. By graphing both sets of data on a single grid, students can see that the point at which the costs are the same is where the graphs cross. One can infer that values closer to the bottom of the graph at a particular point represent lower cost. Or students can make a table for the graph by first choosing an easy value to read, such as 20 bikes for $600. Then they can find that renting 1 bike costs $30; thus, by multiplying any number of bikes by 30, they can complete the table.

B. No. One can only rent whole numbers of bikes.

For the Teacher This question is intended to help students realize an important difference between graphs of discrete variables and graphs of continuous variables. Speed and time are continuous variables, and it makes sense to connect the points since a fraction of a minute is possible. Bikes are discrete variables. It would not make sense to rent part of a bicycle.

C. Because Adrian's graph appears to be linear, the price at Adrian's is $30 per bike. Thus, the cost of renting 32 bikes will be $30 × 32, or $960. Cost estimates for Rocky's will vary. Here is one possible way to reason: The per-bike price for 30 bikes is $975 ÷ 30, or $32.50. The per-bike price for 35 bikes is $1,070 ÷ 35, or about $30.57. The per-bike price for 32 bikes is between these two prices. If we use $31.50 as an estimate, we get a cost of 32 × $31.50, or $1,008 for 32 bikes.

D. 1. Possible answers: The data for Adrian's appear to form a straight-line graph. This indicates that rental prices at Adrian's increases at a constant rate as the number of bikes increases. Using the fact that 20 bikes cost $600, we can see that Adrian's charges $30 per bike. Rocky's charges a lot for the first five bikes but, with each additional five bikes, the additional charge decreases.

2. For Adrian's bike shop just multiply the number of bikes by $30. For Rocky's you have to estimate how the cost is declining as the number of bikes increases.

E. 1. Multiply the number of bikes by $30.

2. Possible answer: Find the price per bike for a number of bikes above and below the number you are interested in. Use these two prices to estimate the per-bike price for the number of bikes you want to rent. Then, multiply by the number of bikes. If the number of bikes is greater than the number in the table, students can start with the facts that the per-bike cost for 50 bikes is $24 and this price decreases with each bike rented. To make an estimate for a number of bikes close to 50, use $24, or a slightly lower price as the per-bike estimate. If the number of bikes is much greater than 50, use a per-bike price less than $24. However, there has to be a minimum charge.

2.2 Finding Customers

Goals

- Make a graph from a table, choosing the variable and scale for each axis

- Use tables and graphs to analyze data and make decisions

In this problem, students graph data from a table. Although they have made graphs in other problems, this time students must determine which variable goes on which axis and what scale makes sense. After making their graphs, students analyze the data using the graph or table and make a decision about what price the tour operators should charge. This is the second time students see a decreasing pattern of change.

Launch 2.2

Discuss the problem situation with students. This context can be hard for students. To make the situation more real, conduct a quick survey of the class:

- *Let's find out what our class thinks about the bike tour price. Raise your hand if you would pay $150 to go on the bike trip.*

- *Raise your hand if you would pay $200. Raise your hand if you would pay $250?*

Continue for a few more prices, until you feel students have a good understanding of what is happening in the problem.

Do not discuss which variable should be displayed on which axis. Let students figure this out themselves. If students choose to put the number of customers on the x-axis, let them work with this. During the summary, you can discuss how easy or difficult it is to make sense of the data when it is represented in this way. This gives you a chance to informally assess what students understand about choosing variables and scales for the axes of a graph.

We want students to begin thinking about how the price of the tour will affect the number of customers. This problem asks students to think about market research data that can help set the target for number of customers.

Encourage students to work individually to make a graph. When they are done, it works well to pair students to discuss the graphs and complete the rest of the problem.

Explore 2.2

Students may want to redo their graph after talking with their partner. Encourage this.

As you visit different groups, ask how and why they decided which variable to put on each axis. Also encourage students to describe exactly what happens to the number of customers as the price increases by $100, $200, and so on.

If students choose a scale and later find it is not such a good choice, ask why and ask them to share their first and second attempts during the summary. You want the summary to push students to think hard about how to choose independent and dependent variables and scales for a graph. These ideas will be revisited again in Investigation 4, but for graphing calculator graphs.

Have some students draw their graphs on transparent grids to share during the summary.

Summarize 2.2

Have students share their graphs and describe how they chose the variable and scale for each axis.

Suggested Questions Ask students:

- *How would you describe the shape of the graph?* (The points are on a curve that decreases from left to right.)

- *How many people do you think would say yes if the price were $100?* (probably between 76 and 80 people)

If a student puts the number of customers on the x-axis, ask:

- *What are the disadvantages of putting the number of customers on the x-axis?* (The data are exactly the same, but the graph seems to imply that the cost of the tour depends on the number of people rather than the fact that the number of people depends on the price.)

INVESTIGATION 2

Have students share their decisions about what price should be charged. Collect all students' responses and then discuss their reasons for selecting a certain price. Some students may change their choice after listening to another student's reasons.

Suggested Question Ask:

- *For each price, how much money would be collected if the people who said they would go for that price actually do so?*

Elicit from your students why these results are important and interesting, assuming they are one of the partners for the tour company.

Discuss Question D. Make sure students understand how changes show up in a table and in a graph. Also make sure students can talk about how to compute or estimate values in-between data entries in the table. For a cost of $425, they might predict 43 or 44 customers. The rate of decline seems to be getting greater and the last two entries went down by about 10 customers. Because $425 is half way in-between $400 and $450, the number of customers would be about half way between 49 and 38, but could be closer to 38.

2.2 Finding Customers

Mathematical Goals

- Make a graph from a table, choosing the variable and scale for each axis
- Use tables and graphs to analyze data and make decisions

Launch

Discuss the problem situation with students.

Do not discuss which variable should be displayed on which axis. Let students figure this out themselves.

Encourage students to work individually to make a graph and then in pairs to discuss the graphs and complete the problem.

Materials
- Transparency 2.2 (optional)

Explore

Encourage students to redo their graphs after talking to their partners, if they need to.

Challenge students to explain how and why they decided which variable to put on each axis.

If students choose a scale and later find it is not such a good choice, ask why and ask them to share their first and second attempts during the summary.

Have some students draw their graphs on transparent grids to share during the summary.

Materials
- Grid paper
- Transparent grids

Summarize

Have students share their graphs and describe how they chose the variable and scale for each axis.

- *How would you describe the shape of the graph?*
- *How many people do you think would say yes if the price were $100?*

If a student puts the number of customers on the *x*-axis, ask:

- *What are the disadvantages of putting the number of customers on the x-axis?*

Collect students' suggestions for how much the tour operators should charge. Then discuss their reasons for selecting a certain price.

Ask:

- *For each price, how much money would be collected if the people who said they would go for that price actually do so?*

Discuss Question D. Make sure students understand how changes show up in a table and in a graph.

Make sure students can estimate values that fall between data entries.

Materials
- Student notebooks

ACE Assignment Guide for Problem 2.2

Core 6, 22, 23
Other *Applications* 5, 7; *Connections* 17, 18; unassigned choices from earlier problems

Adapted For suggestions about adapting ACE exercises, see the *CMP Special Needs Handbook.*
Connecting to Prior Units 18: *Covering and Surrounding*

Answers to Problem 2.2

A. The number of customers depends on the tour price, so price goes on the *x*-axis and number of customers goes on the *y*-axis.

B.

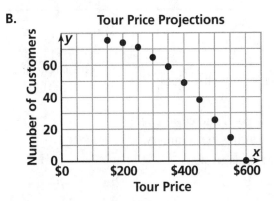

C. Possible answer: $250.

> **For the Teacher** After $250, the number of customers falls off more quickly. You may want to use increments of 5 customers so that the dropoff is more apparent. To help students better understand the situation, encourage them to make a table showing the revenue for each price, like the one at the top of the next column. The revenue is the number of customers times the price. The most revenue is projected for a price of $350.

Encourage students to think of other real-world considerations. For example, the tour might be more successful if the number of customers is less, since people may not want to go on a crowded tour. On the other hand, people will expect more if they pay more, so they might have more dissatisfied customers if they charge too much.

Price	Number of Customers	Revenue (Price × Number of Customers)
$150	76	$11,400
$200	74	$14,800
$250	71	$17,750
$300	65	$19,500
$350	59	$20,650
$400	49	$19,600
$450	38	$17,100
$500	26	$13,000
$550	14	$7,700
$600	0	$0

D. 1. The number of customers decreases as the price increases. The graph is not a straight line, indicating that the decrease in the number of customers is not constant for each $50 price increase. The curve shows that customers are less likely to drop out at a $50 increase when the tour price is lower.

2. In the table, the number of potential customers decreases as you move down. In the graph, the number of customers falls from 76 to 0 as you move from left to right.

3. Possible answer: For $425, they could expect about 42 or 43 customers. $425 is halfway between $400 and $450, so the number of customers would be between 49 and 38. Because the rate of decline is increasing, the number of customers would be closer to 38 than to 49.

Goals

- Predict the pattern in the graph of a relationship between variables

- Tell the "story" shown in a graph

This section addresses the issues that arise in the interpretation of the "stories" shown in graphs. The problem asks students to think about how pairs of variables might be related and to choose the graph that best represents the story of the relationship. The problem gives students practice reading the patterns of change shown by graphs. The emphasis is not on specific numerical values of data points, but on the pattern of change shown by the overall shape of the graph, the slopes of segments of the graph, and so on.

Launch 2.3

Tell students that today they will practice reading "stories" shown in graphs. Discuss the introduction to the problem, including the questions students should ask themselves when they look at a graph.

Discuss the Getting Ready, which gives two possible graphs for how the number of cars in a school parking lot changes during the course of a typical school day. Allow students to share their ideas. Ask them to talk about what each graph would mean in the context of the situation.

- *Describe the "story" each graph tells about the school parking lot. Which graph shows the pattern you expect?* (In Graph 1, a few cars park in the lot early in the day, but then there is no change for a period of time. In the middle of the day, there is a sharp increase in the number of cars, followed immediately by a sharp decrease. There is a constant, small number of cars for a while, and then those cars leave and the lot is empty. In Graph 2, there is a steady increase in the number of cars early in the day. The number of cars levels off and is constant for most of the day. Then, there is a steady decrease in the number of cars until the lot is empty. Graph 2 is what I would expect for a school parking lot, where teachers park their cars in the morning, leave them in the parking lot for the school day, and then drive them home in the evening.

- *How could you label the graph you chose so that someone else would know what it represented?* (Label the *x*-axis "Time" and the *y*-axis "Number of Cars." Add the title "Cars in School Parking Lot.")

Read the steps at the beginning of the Problem 2.3 and make sure students know what to do. Make sure students understand that they can sketch their own graph if they don't think any of the given graphs is a good match. You may not want your students to take the time to write out explanations for every graph. However, tell them they should be prepared to explain why they made the matches they did.

Let the students work alone for a minute or two, and then move them into small groups of 2 to 4. This gives each student time to think individually before discussing ideas with a group.

Explore 2.3

Suggested Questions If students are having difficulty, ask them questions like those below. Emphasize that these are the types of questions they should ask themselves.

- *Which variable depends on the other?*

- *As the independent variable increases, what happens to the dependent variable? Does it increase or decrease?*

- *Will the increase or decrease be constant or will it slow down or speed up in some places?*

- *How will the change appear in the graph moving left to right?*

- *Is the graph likely to repeat in cycles?*

Ask students to defend their choices as you move from group to group. You are looking for reasonable interpretations, not for agreement on one graph as the "right" answer. This will tell you a lot about what sense students are making of how stories of change can be portrayed in graphs.

Summarize 2.3

Have students "talk their way along" the graphs to explain why they chose the matches they did. For example, for the bathtub situation in Question C, which matches Graph 1, students should explain that the first upward sloping segment shows the water level as the tub fills at a constant rate. The first horizontal segment shows the level after the water is turned off, but before the person steps into the tub. The vertical segment shows the water level rising almost instantaneously when the person gets in the tub. The horizontal segment represents the constant water level when the bather is soaking. The next vertical segment shows the water level falling as the person gets out of the tub. The last, slanted segment shows the water level steadily falling as the tub drains.

If you did not require your students to write out explanations, you might ask them to choose one or two matches and explain them as part of their homework.

Check for Understanding

Have students sketch a graph that shows something in their lives changing over time. Students can share their graph and have others try to think what story it could be telling.

2.3 What's the Story?

Mathematical Goals

- Predict the pattern in the graph of a relationship between variables
- Tell the "story" shown in a graph

Launch

Discuss the introduction to the problem, including the questions students should ask themselves when they look at a graph.

Discuss the Getting Ready.

Explain the tasks in Problem 2.3.

Have students work alone before moving into small groups of 2 to 4.

Materials
- Transparency 2.3A

Explore

If students are having difficulty, ask them questions like those below. Emphasize that these are the types of questions they should ask themselves.

- *Which variable depends on the other?*
- *As the independent variable increases, what happens to the dependent variable? Does it increase or decrease?*
- *Will the increase or decrease be constant or will it slow down or speed up in some places?*
- *How will the change appear in the graph moving left to right?*
- *Is the graph likely to repeat in cycles?*

Have students defend their choices as you move from group to group. Look for reasonable interpretations.

Summarize

Have students "talk their way along" the graphs to explain why they chose the matches they did.

If you did not require your students to write out explanations, you might ask them to choose one or two matches and explain them as part of their homework.

Check for Understanding

Have students sketch a graph that shows something in their lives changing over time. Students can share their graph and have others try to think what story it could be telling.

Materials
- Student notebooks
- Transparency 2.3B

ACE Assignment Guide for Problem 2.3

Core 8, 10–12
Other *Applications* 9, 13, 14; *Connections* 19; *Extensions* 24; unassigned choices from earlier problems

Adapted For suggestions about adapting ACE exercises, see the *CMP Special Needs Handbook.*
Connecting to Prior Units 24: *Shapes and Designs*

Answers to Problem 2.3

Answers may vary. The most likely matches are given below. However, any match students can give a reasonable explanation for should be considered correct.

A. Graph 2. Possible answers: The *x*-axis represents the price of the trip, and the *y*-axis represents the number of students. The number of students decreases when the price of the trip increases. The title might be Estimated Trip Attendance.

B. Graph 6. Possible answers: The *x*-axis represents the time, and the *y*-axis represents the speed. At the beginning, when the skateboard rider goes down, her speed increases quickly as time passes. The speed is at its peak when the rider is at the bottom of the ramp, then it decreases quickly as she goes up the other side. The title might be Skater's Speed.

For the Teacher Make sure students understand why Graph 5, which shows the speed diminishing and then increasing, is not correct. This problem reminds students that a graph is a picture of a set of data pairs, not a literal picture of a scene involved in a problem.)

C. Graph 1. Possible answer: The *x*-axis represents time, and the *y*-axis represents the water level. The first upward sloping segment shows the water level as the tub fills at a constant rate. The first horizontal segment shows the level after the water is turned off, but before the person steps into it. The vertical segment shows the water level rising almost instantaneously when the person gets in the tub. The horizontal segment represents the constant water level when the bather is soaking. The next vertical segment shows the water level falling as the person gets out of the tub. The last, slanted segment shows the water level steadily falling as the tub drains. The title might be Water Level in a Tub.

D. Graph 4. Possible answer: The *x*-axis represents the number of people in the park, and the *y*-axis represents the waiting time. The waiting time increases as the number of people in the park increases. The title might be Waiting Time for a Ride.

E. Graph 3. Possible answer: The *x*-axis represents time, and the *y*-axis represents the number of hours of daylight. Daylight change in a periodic pattern as the seasons change. Graph 3 shows what would happen over about two years, beginning in the start of spring and ending about the start of fall. The number of hours of daylight increases from spring to summer and then decreases from summer to winter and increases again from winter to spring. This pattern happens each year. The title might be Number of Hours of Daylight.

F. Graph 2. Possible answer: The *x*-axis represents time, and the *y*-axis represents the weekly attendance. The weekly attendance decreases as the time passes. The title might be Weekly Attendance at a Movie.

G. Graph 4 (or Graph 5 if students assume people won't come if it is too hot). Possible answer: The *x*-axis represents the predicted high temperature, and the *y*-axis represents the number of customers. The number of customers increases as the predicted temperature increases. The title might be Number of Customers.

The student edition pages for this investigation begin on the next page.

Notes _____
_____
_____
_____

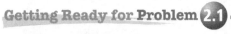

Investigation 2

Analyzing Graphs and Tables

In this investigation you will continue to use tables, graphs, and descriptions to compare information and make decisions. Using tables, graphs, and words to represent relationships is an important part of algebra.

Sidney, Celia, Liz, Malcolm, and Theo continue making plans for Ocean Bike Tours. Many of these plans involve questions about money.

> *How much will it cost to operate the tours?*

> *How much should customers pay?*

> *Will the company make a profit?*

The five tour operators decide to do some research.

Getting Ready for Problem 2.1

- With your classmates, make a list of things the tour operators must provide for their customers. Estimate the cost of each item per customer.

- Estimate how much customers would be willing to pay for the three-day tour.

- Based on your estimates, will the partners earn a profit?

30   Variables and Patterns

Notes _____

_____

_____

_____

2.1 Renting Bicycles

The tour operators decide to rent bicycles for their customers. They get information from two bike shops.

Rocky's Cycle Center sends a table of weekly rental fees for bikes.

Rocky's Weekly Rental Rates for Bikes

Number of Bikes	5	10	15	20	25	30	35	40	45	50
Rental Fee	$400	$535	$655	$770	$875	$975	$1,070	$1,140	$1,180	$1,200

Adrian's Bike Shop sends a graph of their weekly rental fees. Because the rental fee depends on the number of bikes, they put the number of bikes on the *x*-axis.

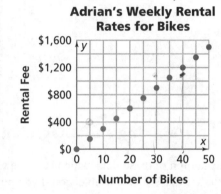

Adrian's Weekly Rental Rates for Bikes

Problem 2.1 **Analyzing a Table and a Graph**

A. Which bike shop should Ocean Bike Tours use? Explain.

B. Suppose you make a graph from the table for Rocky's Cycle Center. Would it make sense to connect the points? Explain.

C. How much do you think each company charges to rent 32 bikes?

D. 1. What patterns do you find in the table and in the graph?

    2. Based on the patterns you found in part (1), how can you predict values that are not included in the table or graph?

E. 1. Describe a way to find the costs for renting any number of bikes from Adrian's Bike Shop.

    2. Describe a way to find the costs for renting any number of bikes from Rocky's Cycle Center.

ACE Homework starts on page 35.

Notes _____

_____

_____

_____

2.2 Finding Customers

The tour operators plan a route and choose a bike shop. Now they must figure out what price to charge so they can attract customers and make a profit.

To help set a price, they conduct a survey. They ask 100 people who have taken other bicycle tours which of the following amounts they would pay for the Ocean Bike Tour: $150, $200, $250, $300, $350, $400, $450, $500, $550, or $600. The results are shown in the table below.

Problem 2.2 Making and Analyzing a Graph

A. To make a graph of these data, which variable would you put on the *x*-axis? Which variable would you put on the *y*-axis? Explain.

B. Make a coordinate graph of the data on grid paper.

C. Based on your graph, what price do you think the tour operators should charge? Explain.

D. 1. The number of people who say they would take the tour depends on the price. How does the number of potential customers change as the price increases?

    2. How is the change in the number of potential customers shown in the table? How is the change shown on the graph?

    3. Describe a way to find the number of potential customers for a price between two prices in the table. For example, how can you predict the number of customers for a price of $425?

ACE Homework starts on page 35.

Price Customers Would Pay

Total Price	Number of Customers
$150	76
$200	74
$250	71
$300	65
$350	59
$400	49
$450	38
$500	26
$550	14
$600	0

32 Variables and Patterns

What's the Story?

It's important to be good at reading the "story" in a graph. Remember that the y-axis, or vertical axis, of a graph usually represents the *dependent variable*, and the x-axis, or horizontal axis, represents the *independent variable*. Here are some questions to ask when you look at a graph.

> *What are the variables represented by the graph?*
>
> *Do the values of one variable seem to depend on the values of the other? In other words, do changes in one variable seem to be the result of changes in the other?*
>
> *What does the shape of the graph say about the relationship between the variables?*

Getting Ready for Problem

The number of cars in a school parking lot changes as time passes during a school day. These graphs show two possibilities for the way the number of cars might change over time.

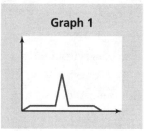

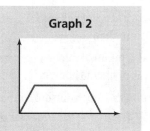

- Describe the "story" each graph tells about the school parking lot. Which graph shows the pattern you expect?

- How could you label the graph you chose so that someone else would know what it represents?

Investigation 2 Analyzing Graphs and Tables **33**

STUDENT PAGE

Notes _____

_____

_____

_____

STUDENT PAGE

STUDENT PAGE

Problem 2.3 Interpreting Graphs

Questions A–G describe pairs of related variables. For each pair,

- Decide which variable is the dependent variable and which is the independent variable.
- Find a graph that tells a reasonable "story" about how the variables might be related. If no graph tells a reasonable story, sketch your own.
- Explain what the graph tells about the relationship of the variables.
- Give the graph a title.

A. The *number of students* who go on a school trip is related to the *price of the trip* for each student.

B. When a skateboard rider goes down one side of a half-pipe ramp and up the other side, her *speed* changes as *time* passes.

C. The *water level* changes over *time* when someone fills a tub, takes a bath, and empties the tub.

D. The *waiting time* for a popular ride at an amusement park is related to the *number of people in the park*.

E. The *number of hours of daylight* changes over *time* as the seasons change.

F. *Weekly attendance* at a popular movie changes as *time* passes from the date the movie first appears in theaters.

G. The *number of customers* at an amusement park with water slides is related to the *predicted high temperature* for the day.

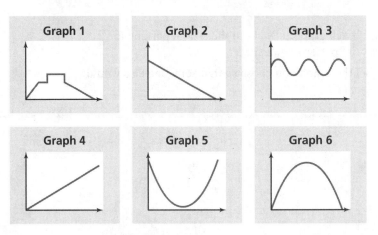

Graph 1 Graph 2 Graph 3

Graph 4 Graph 5 Graph 6

ACE Homework starts on page 35.

34 Variables and Patterns

Notes _____

_____

_____

_____

Applications

1. Use the table to answer parts (a)–(e).

Typical Weights for Tiger Cubs	
Age (weeks)	Expected Body Weight (kg)
birth	1.3
1	2.3
2	3.0
3	3.8
4	4.5
5	5.2
6	6.0
7	6.7
8	7.5
9	7.6
10	8.9
11	9.7

SOURCE: www.tigerlink.org

a. What weight is predicted for a 1-week-old tiger cub?

b. What weight is predicted for a 10-week-old tiger cub?

c. At what age do tiger cubs typically weigh 7 kilograms?

d. Describe the pattern relating age and weight. Do you expect this pattern to continue indefinitely?

e. Would it make sense to connect the points in a graph of these data?

Investigation 2 Analyzing Graphs and Tables   **35**

Notes _____

_____

_____

_____

2. Dezi researches DVD rental prices at local video stores. Source Video has a yearly membership package. The manager gives Dezi this table:

Source Video Membership/Rental Packages

Number of DVDs Rented	0	5	10	15	20	25	30
Total Cost	$30	$35	$40	$45	$50	$55	$60

Supreme Video does not have membership packages. Dezi makes the graph below to relate the cost at Supreme Video to the number of DVDs rented.

a. Both video stores have a good selection of movies. Dezi's family plans to watch about two movies a month. Which video store should they choose?

b. Write a paragraph explaining to Dezi how he can decide which video store to use.

c. For each store, describe the pattern of change relating the number of DVDs rented to the cost.

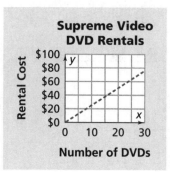

Supreme Video DVD Rentals

3. The table shows the fees charged at one of the campgrounds on the Ocean Bike Tour.

Campground Fees

Number of Campsites	1	2	3	4	5	6	7	8
Total Campground Fee	$12.50	$25.00	$37.50	$50.00	$62.50	$75.00	$87.50	$100.00

a. Make a coordinate graph of the data.

b. Does it make sense to connect the points on your graph? Explain.

c. Using the table, describe the pattern of change in the total campground fee as the number of campsites increases.

d. How is the pattern you described in part (c) shown in your graph?

Notes

_____

_____

_____

_____

4. Some class officers want to sell T-shirts to raise funds for a class trip. They ask the students in their class how much they would pay for a shirt and record the data in a table.

Projected Shirt Sales

Price per Shirt	$5	$10	$15	$20	$25
Number of Shirt Sales	50	40	30	20	10

a. Describe the relationship between the price per shirt and the expected number of shirt sales. Is this the sort of pattern you would expect?

b. Copy and complete this table to show the relationship between price per shirt and the expected total value of the shirt sales.

Projected Shirt Sales

Price per Shirt	$5	$10	$15	$20	$25
Number of Shirt Sales	50	40	30	20	10
Value of Shirt Sales	$250	$400	■	■	■

c. How would you describe the relationship between price per shirt and expected total value of shirt sales? Is this the sort of pattern you would expect?

d. Use grid paper to make coordinate graphs of the data like the ones started below.

e. Explain how your answers to parts (a) and (c) are shown in the graphs.

Notes _____

_____

_____

_____

5. A camping-supply store rents camping gear for $25 per person.

   a. Make a table of the total rental charges for 0, 5, 10, 15, 20, 25, 30, 35, 40, 45, and 50 campers.

   b. Make a coordinate graph using the data in your table.

   c. Compare the pattern of change in your table and graph with patterns you found in Exercise 3. Describe the similarities and differences between the two sets of data.

6. The tour operators need to rent a truck to transport camping gear, clothes, and bicycle repair equipment. They check prices at two truck-rental companies.

   a. East Coast Trucks charges $4.25 for each mile driven. Make a table of the charges for 0, 25, 50, 75, 100, 125, 150, 175, 200, 225, 250, 275, and 300 miles.

   b. Philadelphia Truck Rental charges $40 per day and an additional $2.00 for each mile driven. Make a table of the charges for renting a truck for five days and driving it 0, 25, 50, 75, 100, 125, 150, 175, 200, 225, 250, 275, and 300 miles.

   c. On one coordinate grid, plot the charge plans for both rental companies. Use a different color to mark each company's plan.

   d. Based on your work in parts (a)–(c), which company offers the better deal? Explain.

38   Variables and Patterns

Notes _____

_____

_____

_____

7. The table shows fees for using a campsite at a state park from 1 day up to the park limit of 10 days.

Campsite Fees

Days of Use	1	2	3	4	5	6	7	8	9	10
Campsite Fee	$20	$30	$40	$50	$60	$70	$75	$80	$85	$90

   a. Make a coordinate graph using the table.

   b. Does it make sense to connect the points on your graph? Why or why not?

   c. Describe the pattern relating the variables *days of use* and *campsite fee*.

8. Suppose a motion detector tracks the time and the distance traveled as you walk 40 feet in 8 seconds. Match the following (*time, distance*) graphs with the "stories" that describe each walk.

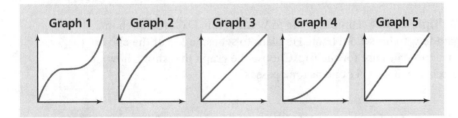

Graph 1   Graph 2   Graph 3   Graph 4   Graph 5

   a. You walk at a steady pace of 5 feet per second.

   b. You walk slowly at first and then steadily increase your walking speed.

   c. You walk rapidly at first, pause for several seconds, and then walk at an increasing rate for the rest of the trip.

   d. You walk at a steady rate for 3 seconds, pause for 2 seconds, and then walk at a steady rate for the rest of the trip.

   e. You walk rapidly at first, but gradually slow down as the end of the trip nears.

9. For each walk in Exercise 8, complete a (*time, distance*) table like the one below. Use numbers that will match the pattern of the walk and its graph.

Time (seconds)	1	2	3	4	5	6	7	8
Distance (feet)	■	■	■	■	■	■	■	40

Notes

10. The graphs below show five patterns of change in the price per gallon of gasoline. Match each (*time, price*) graph with the "story" it tells.

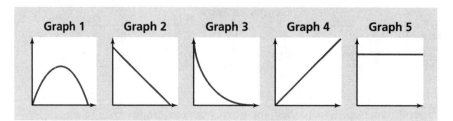

Graph 1   Graph 2   Graph 3   Graph 4   Graph 5

   a. The price declined at a steady rate.

   b. The price did not change.

   c. The price rose rapidly, then leveled off for a while, and then declined rapidly.

   d. The price rose at a steady rate.

   e. The price dropped rapidly at first and then at a slower rate.

11. Multiple Choice Jamie is going to Washington, D.C., to march in a parade with his school band. He plans to set aside $25 at the end of each month to use for the trip. Choose the graph that shows how Jamie's savings will build as time passes.

A.
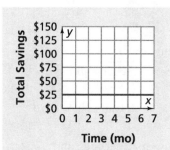

B.
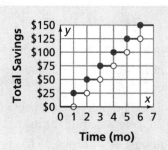

C.
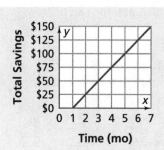

D. None of these is correct.

Notes _____

_____

_____

_____

12. The graph shows how the temperature changed during an all-day hike by students.

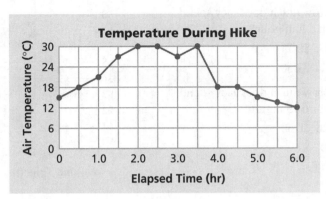

Temperature During Hike

a. What was the maximum temperature and when did it occur?

b. When was the temperature rising most rapidly?

c. When was the temperature falling most rapidly?

d. When was the temperature about 24°C?

e. The hikers encounter a thunderstorm with rain. When do you think this happened?

Investigation 2 Analyzing Graphs and Tables   **41**

Notes _____

_____

_____

_____

Jacy works at a department store. This graph shows parking costs at the parking garage Jacy uses.

13. **Multiple Choice** How much does Jacy spend to park for less than a half hour?

   F. $0.50   **G.** $0.75

   H. $1   **J.** $1.50

14. **Multiple Choice** How much does Jacy spend to park for 4 hours and 15 minutes?

   A. $6   **B.** $6.50

   C. $6.75   **D.** $7

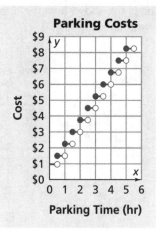

Parking Costs

Connections

15. The area of a rectangle is the product of its length and its width.

   a. Find all whole number pairs of length and width values that give an area of 24 square meters. Record the pairs in a table.

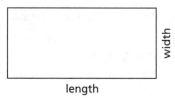

length

width

Rectangles with an Area of 24 m²

Length	■	■	■	...
Width	■	■	■	...

   b. Make a coordinate graph of the (*length, width*) data from part (a).

   c. Connect the points on your graph if it makes sense to do so. Explain your decision.

   d. Describe the relationship between length and width for rectangles of area 24 square meters.

16. The perimeter of any rectangle is the sum of its side lengths.

   a. Make a table of all possible whole-number pairs of length and width values for a rectangle with a perimeter of 18 meters.

   b. Make a coordinate graph of the (*length, width*) data from part (a).

   c. Connect the points on your graph if it makes sense to do so. Explain your decision.

   d. Describe the relationship between length and width for rectangles of perimeter 18 meters, and explain how that relationship is shown in the table and graph.

Homework
Help **O**nline
━ PHSchool.com
For: Help with Exercise 16
Web Code: ane-1216

42 Variables and Patterns

Notes _____

_____

_____

_____

17. The table below shows the winners and the winning times for the women's Olympic 400-meter dash since 1964.

Women's Olympic 400-meter Dash		
Year	Name	Time (seconds)
1964	Celia Cuthbert, AUS	52.0
1968	Colette Besson, FRA	52.0
1972	Monika Zehrt, E. GER	51.08
1976	Irena Szewinska, POL	49.29
1980	Martia Koch, E. GER	48.88
1984	Valerie Brisco-Hooks, USA	48.83
1988	Olga Bryzgina, USSR	48.65
1992	Marie-Jose Perec, FRA	48.83
1996	Marie-Jose Perec, FRA	48.25
2000	Cathy Freeman, AUS	49.11
2004	Tonique Williams-Darling, BAH	49.41

a. Make a coordinate graph of the (*year, time*) information. Choose a scale that allows you to see the differences between the winning times.

b. What patterns do you see in the table and graph? Do the winning times seem to be rising or falling? In which year was the best time earned?

18. The circumference of a circle is related to its radius by the formula $C = 2 \times \pi \times r$. The area of a circle is related to its radius by the formula $A = \pi \times r^2$.

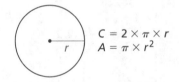

$$C = 2 \times \pi \times r$$
$$A = \pi \times r^2$$

a. Make a table showing how the circumference of a circle increases as the radius increases in 1-unit steps from 1 to 6. Make sure to express the circumferences in terms of π. Then describe the pattern relating those two variables.

b. Make a table showing how the area of a circle increases as the radius increases in 1-unit steps from 1 to 6. Make sure to express the areas in terms of π. Then describe the pattern relating those two variables.

Investigation 2 Analyzing Graphs and Tables   **43**

Notes _____

_____

_____

_____

19. Here are the box-office earnings for a movie during each of the first eight weeks following its release.

Box Office Earnings

Weeks in Theaters	1	2	3	4	5	6	7	8
Weekly Earnings (millions)	$16	$22	$18	$12	$7	$4	$3	$1

a. Make a coordinate graph showing the weekly earnings after each week. Because a film's weekly earnings depend on the number of weeks it is in theaters, put the weeks in theaters on the *x*-axis and the weekly earnings on the *y*-axis.

b. Explain how the weekly earnings changed as time passed. How is this pattern of change shown in the table and the graph? Why might this change have occurred?

c. What were the total earnings of the movie in the eight weeks?

d. Make a coordinate graph showing the total earnings after each week.

e. Explain how the movie's total earnings changed over time. How is this pattern of change shown in the table and the graph? Why might this change have occurred?

Extensions

20. Use what you know about decimals to find coordinates of five points that lie on the line segment between the labeled points on each graph:

a.
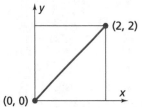

b.
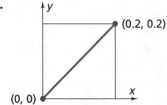

Notes _____

_____

_____

_____

21. The graphs below each show relationships between independent
   (*x*-axis) and dependent (*y*-axis) variables. However, the scales on the
   coordinate axes are not the same for all the graphs.

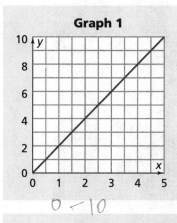

0 ~ 10

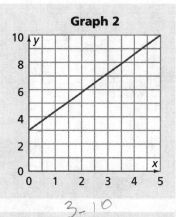

3 - 10

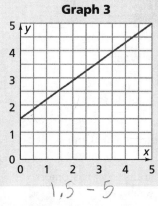

1,5 - 5

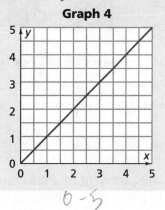

0 - 5

a. Which graph shows the dependent variable increasing most rapidly
   as the independent variable increases?

b. Which graph shows the dependent variable increasing most slowly
   as the independent variable increases?

Notes _____

_____

_____

_____

22. To raise money, students plan to hold a car wash. They ask some adults how much they would pay for a car wash. The table below shows the results of their research.

Price Customers Would Pay for a Car Wash

Car Wash Price	$4	$6	$8	$10	$12	$14
Number of Customers	120	105	90	75	60	45

a. Make a coordinate graph of the (*price, customers*) data. Connect the points if it makes sense to do so.

b. Describe the pattern relating the price to the number of customers. Explain how the table and the graph show the pattern.

c. Based on the pattern, what number of customers would you predict if the price were $16? What number would you predict if the price were $20? What if the price were $2?

23. a. Copy and complete the table below, using the information from Exercise 22.

Projected Car Wash Income

Car Wash Price	$4	$6	$8	$10	$12	$14
Number of Customers	120	105	90	75	60	45
Projected Income	■	■	■	■	■	■

b. Make a graph of the (*price, projected income*) data. Connect the points if it makes sense to do so.

46 Variables and Patterns

Notes _____

_____

_____

_____

c. Describe the pattern relating the price and the projected income. Explain how the table and the graph show the pattern. Explain why the pattern does or does not make business sense to you.

d. Suppose the shopping center where the students plan to hold the car wash will charge the students $1.50 per car for water and cleaning supplies. How can you use this factor to find the profit from the car wash for various prices?

24. Adriana is at a skateboard park that has tracks shaped like regular polygons. Recall that a *regular polygon* is a polygon with congruent sides and congruent angles. Here are some examples:

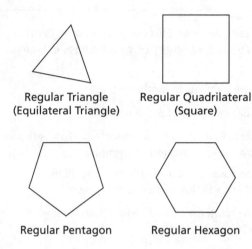

Regular Triangle   Regular Quadrilateral
(Equilateral Triangle)   (Square)

Regular Pentagon   Regular Hexagon

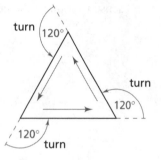

At each vertex of a track, Adriana must make a turn. The size of the turn relates to the number of sides in the polygon. For example, at each vertex of the triangle track, she must make a 120° turn.

a. Copy and complete the table below to show how the size of the turn Adriana must make at each vertex is related to the number of sides of the polygon.

Track Turns

Number of Sides	3	4	5	6	7	8	9	10
Degrees in Turn	120	■	■	■	■	■	■	■

b. Make a coordinate graph of the (*sides, degrees*) data.

c. What pattern of change do you see in the degrees Adriana must turn as the number of sides increases? How does the table show that pattern? How does the graph show that pattern?

Investigation 2 Analyzing Graphs and Tables   **47**

Notes _____

_____

_____

_____

Mathematical Reflections 2

The problems in this investigation asked you to think about *patterns* relating the values of *variables*. These questions will help you to summarize what you have learned.

Think about your answers to these questions. Discuss your ideas with other students and your teacher. Then write a summary of your findings in your notebook.

1. Explain what the word *variable* means in mathematics.

2. What does it mean to say that two variables are related?

3. **a.** Suppose the *y*-values increase as the *x*-values increase. How is this indicated in a table? How is this indicated in a graph?

   b. Suppose the *y*-values decrease as the *x*-values increase. How is this indicated in a table? How is this indicated in a graph?

4. In a coordinate graph of two related variables, when does it make sense to connect the points?

Notes _____

_____

_____

_____

nvestigation

ACE
Assignment Choices

Differentiated Instruction
Solutions for All Learners

Problem 2.1

Core 3, 4, 16
Other *Applications* 1, 2; *Connections* 15; *Extensions* 20, 21; unassigned choices from earlier problems

Problem 2.2

Core 6, 22, 23
Other *Applications* 5, 7; *Connections* 17, 18; unassigned choices from earlier problems

Problem 2.3

Core 8, 10–12
Other *Applications* 9, 13, 14; *Connections* 19; *Extensions* 24; unassigned choices from earlier problems

Adapted For suggestions about adapting Exercise 2 and other ACE exercises, see the CMP *Special Needs Handbook*
Connecting to Prior Units 15, 16, 18: *Covering and Surrounding*; 24: *Shapes and Designs*

Applications

1. a. About 2.3 kilograms

   b. About 8.9 kilograms

   c. Between 7 and 8 weeks

   d. As age increases, weight increases. However, as the cubs approach adulthood, we would expect the weight to level off at some point. The weight will not increase indefinitely.

   e. It makes sense to connect the points because there are tiger cubs whose ages are between weeks.

2. a. Source Video

   b. Possible answer: The graph below shows prices at both stores. The two lines cross at 20 videos. This means that if you rent

20 videos, the price will be the same for both stores. For fewer than 20 videos, Supreme Video is the best value. For more than 20 videos, Source Video is cheaper.

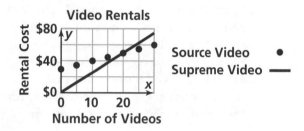

c. Possible answer: To rent videos from Source Video, you pay $30 plus $1 for each video you rent. Supreme Video has no initial fee, and each video costs $2.50, so video rental is $2.50 times the number of videos rented.

3. a.

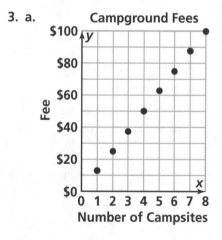

b. No. It does not make sense to talk about fractional parts of campsites.

   For the Teacher It is important to realize this, but that does not mean a graph is "wrong" if the points are connected to see the pattern more clearly.)

c. The total fee increases by $12.50 for each additional campsite.

ACE ANSWERS 2

d. Possible answer: To get from one point to the next, you move right 1 unit and up 12.5 units. This shows that for every increase of 1 campsite, the price increases by $12.50. That is the same pattern shown in the table.

4. a. As the price per shirt increases by $5, the projected number of shirt sales decreases by 10. This is the pattern that is expected in most cases.

b. (Figure 1)

c. Possible answer: The projected value of the shirt sales reaches its maximum at $15 per shirt, then it decreases. Given the data in the first table, this pattern might be expected. However, it is a bit surprising that the decline in numbers of shirts sold overcomes the effect of increasing price per shirt.

d.

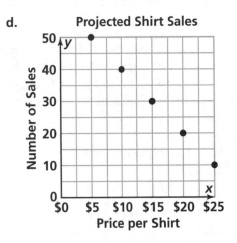

Projected Shirt Sales

e. The first graph shows a decline in number of shirt sales as the per-shirt price increase. The second graph shows an increase in dollar value of shirt sales for increasing per shirt prices up to $15, and then a decrease in total value as the per-shirt price increases beyond that. These are the same relationships described in parts (a) and (c).

5. a.

Camping Gear Rental

Number of Campers	Gear Rental Fee
0	$0
5	$125
10	$250
15	$375
20	$500
25	$625
30	$750
35	$875
40	$1,000
45	$1,125
50	$1,250

b.

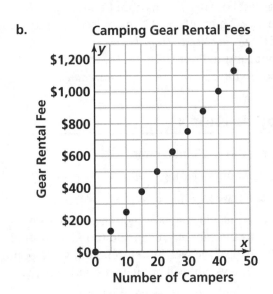

Camping Gear Rental Fees

Figure 1

Projected Shirt Sales

Price per Shirt	$5	$10	$15	$20	$25
Number of Shirt Sales	50	40	30	20	10
Values of Shirt Sales	$250	$400	$450	$400	$250

c. The points on both graphs form straight lines, showing that the dependent variable (campground fee or gear-rental fee) increases by a constant amount as the independent variable (number of campsites or number of campers) increases by a constant amount. In other words, the rate of change is constant in both graphs. In the campsite fee graph, the number of campsites increases in increments of 1. In the camping-gear fee graph, the number of campers increases in increments of 5. The amount of change in the *y*-variables is also different in the two graphs.

6. a.

East Coast Trucks Charges

Distance (mi)	Rental Fee
0	$0
25	$106.25
50	$212.50
75	$318.75
100	$425.00
125	$531.25
150	$637.50
175	$743.75
200	$850.00
225	$956.25
250	$1,062.50
275	$1,168.75
300	$1,275.00

b. Philadelphia Truck Rental Charges

Distance (mi)	Rental Fee
0	$200
25	$250
50	$300
75	$350
100	$400
125	$450
150	$500
175	$550
200	$600
225	$650
250	$700
275	$750
300	$800

c.

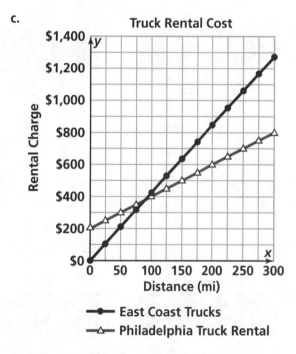

Truck Rental Cost

— East Coast Trucks
—△— Philadelphia Truck Rental

d. If the truck is driven for less than about 89 miles, East Coast Trucks is the company to use. If it is driven more than 89 miles, Philadelphia Truck Rental is the better choice.

7. **a.**

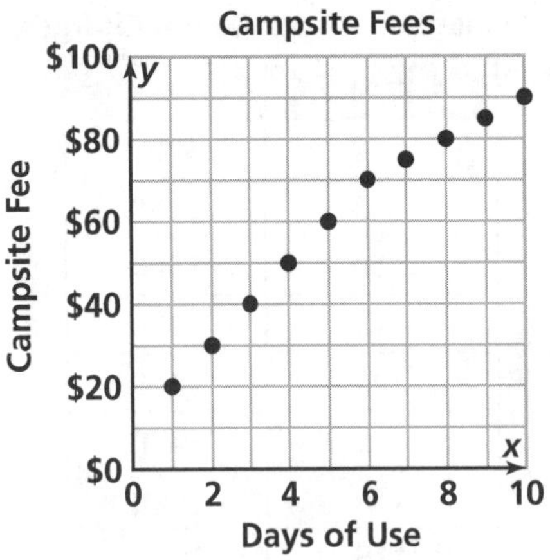

Campsite Fees
Campsite Fee
$100
$80
$60
$40
$20
$0
y
x
0
2
4
6
8
10
Days of Use

b. It probably doesn't make sense to connect the points because one would not ordinarily pay for something less than a whole day.

c. The cost increases at a rate of $10 per day for the first 6 days and at a rate of $5 per day thereafter.

8. **a.** Graph 3
   b. Graph 4
   c. Graph 1
   d. Graph 5
   e. Graph 2

9. There are many different ways to complete most of the required tables. We show one possible solution for each graph. (Figure 2)

Figure 2

Graph 1

Time (seconds)	Distance (feet)
1	9
2	15
3	18
4	20
5	20
6	24
7	31
8	40

Graph 2

Time (seconds)	Distance (feet)
1	9
2	17
3	24
4	30
5	34
6	37
7	39
8	40

Graph 3

Time (seconds)	Distance (feet)
1	5
2	10
3	15
4	20
5	25
6	30
7	35
8	40

Graph 4

Time (seconds)	Distance (feet)
1	1
2	3
3	6
4	10
5	15
6	21
7	29
8	40

Graph 5

Time (seconds)	Distance (feet)
1	$6\frac{2}{3}$
2	$13\frac{1}{3}$
3	20
4	20
5	20
6	$26\frac{2}{3}$
7	$33\frac{1}{3}$
8	40

0. a. Graph 2

   b. Graph 5

   c. Graph 1

   d. Graph 4

   e. Graph 3

1. B

2. a. 30°C; from 2 to 2.5 hours and at 3.5 hours

   b. Between 1.0 and 1.5 hours (a change of 6° per half hour, or 12° per hour)

   c. Between 3.5 and 4.0 hours (a change of 12° per half hour, or 24° per hour)

   d. About 1.25 and 3.75 hours into the hike

   e. The thunderstorm probably hit at about 3.5 hours into the hike because a sharp drop in temperature followed.

3. H

4. C

Connections

5. a.

Length (m)	1	2	3	4	6	8	12	24
Width (m)	24	12	8	6	4	3	2	1

b.

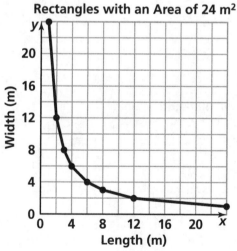

Rectangles with an Area of 24 m²

c. It makes sense to connect the points because there are rectangles with an area of 24 m² that have length and width measurements that are not whole numbers (for example, 16 m and 1.5 m).

d. As the length increases, the width decreases—rapidly at first and then more slowly. The product of length and width is always 24.

16. a.

Length (m)	1	2	3	4	5	6	7	8
Width (m)	8	7	6	5	4	3	2	1

b. Rectangles with a Perimeter of 18 m

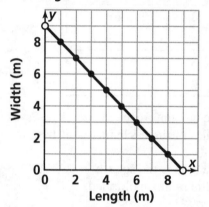

c. It makes sense to connect the points because it is possible to have dimensions that are not whole numbers.

d. Each time the length increases by 1, the width decreases by 1. This is easy to see on the table. On the graph, this is shown by a straight line that slants downward. To move from one point to the next, you go right 1 unit and down 1 unit.

17. a. (Figure 3) (Note that the time scale begins at 48 seconds rather than at 0 seconds.)

b. Possible answer: There was a general pattern of decrease until 1992, with the greatest decrease from 1972 to 1976. After 1976, the decreases level off. The time increased slightly in 1992, decreased in 1996, and increased in 2000 and 2004. The best time of 48.25 seconds was earned in 1996.

18. a.

Radius	Circumference
1	2π
2	4π
3	6π
4	8π
5	10π
6	12π

The circumference increases by 2π as the radius of the circle increases by 1.

b. The area is the square of the radius multiplied by π.

Radius	Area
1	2π
2	4π
3	9π
4	16π
5	25π
6	36π

19. a.

Weekly Box Office Earnings

b. Possible answer: The earnings started fairly high at 16 million the first week, peaked at 22 million the second week, and then gradually decreased to 1 million in the eighth week. The movie's earnings for the first week suggest that there had been good advertisement to create excitement for the film. The second week, more people may have heard about the film and gone to see it. Then, the earnings fell as most of the people who wanted to see the film saw it.

c. $ 83 million

Figure 3

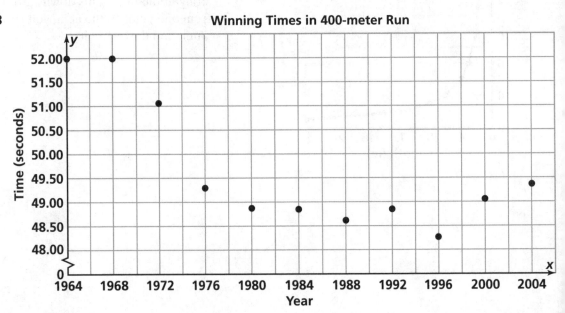

Winning Times in 400-meter Run

d.

Total Box Office Earnings

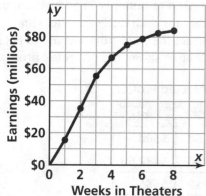

e. The total earnings rose sharply through the third week and then gradually leveled off until the eighth week. The amount of increase is less and less each week. In the table, the weekly earnings decrease as the weeks in the theaters increase. The total earnings increase at a fast rate in the first 3 weeks and then increase slowly as the weeks go on. On the graph, the curved line shows the rate of increase lessening each week. This makes sense because many people who were excited about the movie probably saw it in the opening weeks.

Extensions

0. a. There are many possible answers. Each pair should have identical x- and y-coordinates between 0 and 2. For example, (1.3, 1.3), (0.004, 0.004), and (1.9999, 1.9999).

b. There are many possible answers. Each pair should have identical x- and y-coordinates between 0 and 0.2. For example, (0.1, 0.1), (0.174, 0.174), and (0.08, 0.08).

21. a. Graph 1 shows the greatest rate of increase in y as x increases (an increase of 2 in y for an increase of 1 in x).

b. Graph 3 shows the slowest rate of increase in y as x increases (an increase of 0.75 in y for an increase of 1 in x).

For the Teacher This problem is designed to show that the choice of scales for a graph can affect the visual impression of the relationship.

22. a. While it doesn't make complete sense to connect the points because the number of customers is not a continuous variable, it is quite common to see continuous graphs drawn in such situations.

Results of Car Wash Research

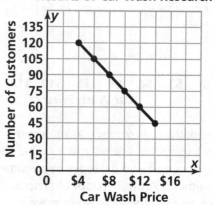

b. For each increase of $2 in price, there is a decrease of 15 customers. The points fall exactly on a line.

c. The pattern suggests that if the price is $16, there will be 30 customers. A price of $20 will attract no customers. A price of $2 will attract 135 customers.

23. a. (Figure 4)

Figure 4

Projected Car-Wash Income

Car Wash Price	$4	$6	$8	$10	$12	$14
Number of Customers	120	105	90	75	60	45
Projected Income	$480	$630	$720	$750	$720	$630

b. It does make some sense to connect the points because prices could be offered at just about any dollar amount (including partial dollars as fine as $0.01).

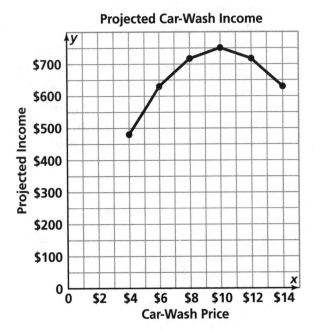

Projected Car-Wash Income

c. The pattern shows increasing income as price increases, but only to a point. Then the price-induced decrease in customers becomes a stronger factor in shaping income than the increase in price itself. The pattern in the data makes sense because if the price goes too high, the number of customers willing to pay this price will decrease. Hence, the income will decrease.

d. To factor in the expense of $1.50 per car, you need to multiply $1.50 by the number of cars (at each different price) and subtract the total from income to get profit. This table shows the projected profits.

Projected Profits

Price	Profit
$4	$300
$6	$472.50
$8	$585
$10	$637.50
$12	$630
$14	$562.50

24. a. (Figure 5)

b.

Skateboard Track Turns

c. Possible answer: As the number of sides increases, the number of degrees in the turn decreases, but not at a steady rate. The number of degrees decreases quickly at first and then by smaller and smaller amounts. On the graph this is shown by a curving pattern of points that decreases rapidly, and then begins to level off. In the table, this is shown by consecutive degree values that get closer and closer together.

Figure 5

Skateboard Track Turns

Number of Sides	3	4	5	6	7	8	9	10
Degrees in Turn	120	90	72	60	51.43	45	40	36

Possible Answers to Mathematical Reflections

1. A variable is a quantity that varies or changes. It can have different measures or values. Age, time, price, height, distance, emotions, and speed are things that can change and have different measures or intensities at different times or for different people. These can all be thought of as variables.

2. When two variables are related, a change in one may affect the other, for example, a person's age and height are related. As your age increases so does your height until you reach maturity. Then your height may decrease as your age continues to increase.

3. **a.** In a table, as the values of x increase, so do the values of y. In a graph, the points rise as you move from left to right.

   b. In a table, as the values of x increase, the values of y decrease. In a graph, the points fall as you move from left to right.

4. When the variable on the x-axis is continuous—that is, when it can take on any value between marked scale values—it often makes sense to connect the points. For example, if the variable on the x-axis is time, it usually makes sense to connect the points because time changes continuously and all the time values between the marked scale values make sense. If the variable on the x-axis takes on only certain, specific values, it generally does not make sense to connect the points. For example, if the variable on the x-axis is number of bikes, it does not make sense to connect the points because only whole numbers of bikes make sense. However, even when it does not make sense to connect the points, connecting them may help you see a pattern. This question will be revisited throughout the rest of this unit.

Investigation 3 — Rules and Equations

Mathematical and Problem-Solving Goals

- Write equations to represent relationships between variables and describe how the pattern of change shows up in a table, a graph, or an equation

- Use tables, graphs, and equations to answer questions

Summary of Problems

Problem 3.1 Writing Equations

Students are introduced to several basic conventions for writing simple (one-step) equations and formulas in symbolic form. Students write equations for the distance traveled at different speeds.

Problem 3.2 Equations with Two Operations

Students write rules and equations involving two arithmetic operations (two-steps). They explore how the pattern of change in a relationship is reflected in the equation, table, and graph of the relationship.

Problem 3.3 Paying Bills and Counting Profits

Students write rules and equations for the revenue, expenses, and profit for the bike tour.

	Suggested Pacing	Materials for Students	Materials for Teachers	ACE Assignments
All	$4\frac{1}{2}$ days	Calculators; blank transparencies (optional); transparent grids (optional)		
3.1	$1\frac{1}{2}$ days	Grid paper; colored pens, pencils or markers	Transparencies 3.1A, 3.1B; colored transparency markers (optional)	1–4, 21–27, 43
3.2	$1\frac{1}{2}$ days		Transparency 3.2	5–12, 28–37, 44–47
3.3	1 day		Transparency 3.3 (optional)	13–20, 38–42, 48, 49
MR	$\frac{1}{2}$ day			

Goals

- Write one-step equations to represent relationships between variables and describe how the pattern of change shows up in a table, a graph, or an equation

- Use tables, graphs, and equations to answer questions

In this problem, students write simple one-step equations to represent relationships between variables. To help them write equations, students first write verbal rules that describe how to calculate values of one variable from values of the other. They then translate their rule to symbolic form, using letters to stand for the variables. Once they have written the equations, they use informal methods to find particular values for the dependent and independent variables. Systematic equation-solving methods are developed in later units.

Launch 3.1

Describe Liz and Malcolm's idea to plan a stop at Wild World amusement park.

Suggested Questions Discuss the Getting Ready questions.

- *What variables do you think are involved in planning for the amusement-park trip?* (Possible answers: number of people on the tour, admission costs, food costs, cost of rides, amount of time riders can spend at the park, weather)

- *How are those variables related to each other?* (Possible answers: The costs for admission, food, and rides are related to the number of people. The costs for food and rides are related to the time spent at the park. The weather is related to the amount of time spent at the park.)

Discuss the example in the student text, which shows how to write a rule for the admission costs first in words, then as an equation with words for the variables, and finally as an equation with single-letter variables. The text also discusses the convention of leaving out the multiplication sign when multiplying a number by a variable or when

multiplying two variables. So, for example, $21 \times n$ may be written as $21n$. Go through the example. Ask questions to help them develop the formula as a group. Use another example if necessary.

When the students seem comfortable with the idea of writing an equation to show how variables are related, move them into small groups to work on the problem.

Explore 3.1

Some students may fill in the distance columns by using an iterative addition process, rather than by multiplying the speed by the time. For example, in the column of distances for 55 mph, they may have added 55 miles (the distance traveled in 1 hour) to each value to get the next value. These students may have difficulty coming up with a general rule linking distance and time. Ask these students how they would find the distance after 11 hours, or 16 hours, or 24 hours. They should see that extending the table to find these distances is tedious and begin to look for a more efficient method.

Suggested Questions If students are having trouble writing the rules and equations, encourage them to focus on the distances for 50 mph first. Ask:

- *What are the variables involved in this relationship?* (time, distance)

- *When you made your table, how did you find the distance for a given time?* (I multiplied 50 mph by the time.)

- *How can you state this as a rule? Start with, "The distance is equal to".* (The distance is equal to 50 times the time traveled.)

- *To write this as an equation, you need to choose letters for the variables. What letters do you want to use?* (d for distance, t for time)

- *How can you write your rule as an equation?* ($d = 50t$)

Remind students that they can refer to the example about the admission costs in their books if they need to.

Have a few groups put their table and graph on transparencies for sharing during the summary.

Have groups share their tables and graphs.

Suggested Questions

- *In the table, how do the distance entries for the three speeds compare? Is this what you would expect?* (For each time, the faster the speed is, the greater the distance is. This makes sense because, if you drive fast for an amount of time, you go farther than if you drive slow.)

- *How do the graphs for the three speeds compare? Why does this make sense?* (For each speed, the points fall on a straight line. The faster the speed, the steeper the line. This makes sense because, for faster speeds, the distance increases faster.)

Have a few students share their rules and equations for parts (1) and (2) of Question C, and discuss the processes they used.

Suggested Questions

- *What steps did you find helpful when you wrote your rules and equations?* (Answers will vary. If students do not mention the usefulness of looking at particular examples, ask whether this was helpful and why.)

- *How did you choose letters for your variables?* (Answers will vary. Most students will use the first letter of the variable name: *d* for distance and *t* for time.) *Did you write down what each letter means so someone reading your work would understand?*

Encourage students to develop the habit of recording their decisions in statements such as, "*d* stands for distance measured in feet, *t* stands for time measured in seconds."

Discuss part (3) of Question C. Make sure the following points are made in the discussion:

- The equations are all of the same form. The only difference is the number *t* is multiplied by. In each case, this number is the speed of the van or the constant pattern of change seen in the table.

- The tables all show a constant pattern of change in distance values. Each time the number of hours increases by 1, the distance increases by a number equal to the speed (which is the distance traveled in 1 hour).

- The graphs all show the same pattern of change. The points are on a straight line, and faster speeds correspond to steeper lines.

NOTE: We are building a foundation for understanding the role of a constant coefficient in a simple linear equation which represents the slope of a line or the constant rate seen in the table.

Question D asks students to find distances traveled at various times. Have students present and explain their solutions. For parts (2) and (3), the easiest way to find the answers is to substitute the time values into the equations. Make sure this is discussed. For example, to find the distance traveled in $4\frac{1}{2}$ hours at 50 miles per hour is:

$$d = 50 \times 4.5 = 225$$

Discuss part (1) of Question E, which asks students to find the time it takes to go a given distance, 320 miles. Allow a variety of solution methods to be presented. Using the equations to answer this question is more difficult than it was for Question D. For the 50 mph case, it requires solving $320 = 50t$. Some students may use a guess-and-check approach or make estimates using the graph or the table. Other students may recognize (from the table or from practical experiences) that the distance divided by the speed equals the time, and calculate $320 \div 50$.

Part (2) adds an additional step. Students must first find $\frac{3}{4}$ of 320 miles, which is 240 miles, and then find the time required to travel that distance. Again, allow a variety of solution methods to be presented.

3.1 Writing Equations

Mathematical Goals

- Write one-step equations to represent relationships between variables and describe how the pattern of change shows up in a table, a graph, or an equation
- Use tables, graphs, and equations to answer questions

Launch

Tell about Liz and Malcolm's idea to plan a stop at Wild World amusement park. Discuss the Getting Ready questions.

Discuss the example in the student text, which shows how to write a rule for the admission costs in words and as an equation. Discuss the convention of leaving out the multiplication sign when multiplying a number by a variable or when multiplying two variables.

Have students work in small groups on the problem.

Materials
- Transparency 3.1A

Vocabulary
- rule
- equation, formula

Explore

If students filled in the distance columns using iterative addition, ask them how they would find the distances after 11, 16, or 24 hours. This should help them focus on finding a more efficient method that involves multiplication.

If students are having trouble writing the rules and equations, encourage them to focus on the distances for 50 mph first.

- *What are the variables involved in this relationship?*
- *When you made your table, how did you find the distance for a given time? How can you state this as a rule? Start with, "The distance is equal to".*
- *To write this as an equation, you need to choose letters for the variables. What letters do you want to use?*
- *How can you write your rule as an equation?*

Summarize

Have students share their tables and graphs.

- *In the table, how do the distance entries for the three speeds compare? Is this what you would expect?*
- *How do the graphs for the three speeds compare? Why does this make sense?*

Have students share their rules and equations from Question C.

- *What steps did you find helpful when you wrote your rules and equations?*
- *How did you choose letters for your variables? Did you write down what each letter means so someone reading your work would understand?*

Have students present and explain their solutions for Question D. Discuss finding distance values by substituting time values into the equation.

Discuss Question E. Allow a variety of solution methods to be presented.

Materials
- Student notebooks
- Transparency 3.1B

ACE Assignment Guide for Problem 3.1

Differentiated Instruction
Solutions for All Learners

Core 1–4
Other *Connections* 21–27, *Extensions* 43

Adapted For suggestions about adapting ACE exercises, see the *CMP Special Needs Handbook*.
Connecting to Prior Units 21, 23, 26: *Covering and Surrounding*; 22: *Data About Us*; 24: *Shapes and Designs*; 25, 27: *Prime Time*

Answers to Problem 3.1

A. (Figure 1)

B.

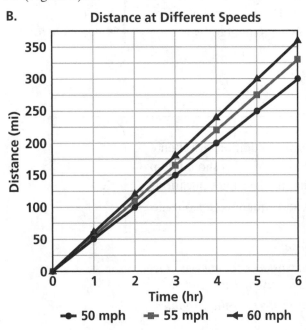

Distance at Different Speeds

— 50 mph   — 55 mph   — 60 mph

C. 1. 50 mph: Distance equals 50 times the time.
55 mph: Distance equals 55 times the time.
60 mph: Distance equals 60 times the time.

2. $d = 50t$, $d = 55t$, $d = 60t$, where d is the distance in miles and t is the time in hours

3. For each speed, the distance increases by a constant amount each hour. In the table, this is shown by the constant difference in consecutive distance values. In the graph, this is shown by a straight-line pattern of points. In the equation, this is shown by the fact that d is equal to a number times t.

D. 1. 150 miles at 50 mph; 165 miles at 55 mph; 180 miles at 60 mph; You can read this directly from the table and estimate from the graph. For the equations, substitute 3 for t and find d.

2. 225 miles at 50 mph; 247.5 miles at 55 mph; 270 miles at 60 mph; In the table, this is the distance value halfway between the distance values for 4 hours and 5 hours. In the graph, draw a line through the set of points and find the y-coordinate of the point with x-coordinate of 4.5. To use the equations, substitute 4.5 for t and find d.

3. 262.5 miles at 50 mph; 288.75 miles at 55 mph; 315 miles at 60 mph; In the table, this is the distance $\frac{1}{4}$ of the way between the distance values for 5 hours and 6 hours. In the graph, draw a line through the set of points and find the y-coordinate of the point with a x-coordinate of 5.25. For the equations, substitute 5.25 for t and solve for d.

E. 1. $6\frac{2}{5}$ hr (or 6 hr 24 min) at 50 mph; $5\frac{9}{11}$ hr (or 5 hr 49 min) at 55 mph; $5\frac{1}{3}$ hr (or 5 hr 20 min) at 60 mph

2. $4\frac{4}{5}$ hr (or 4 hr 48 min) at 50 mph; $4\frac{4}{11}$ hr (or 4 hr 22 min) at 55 mph; 4 hr at 60 mph

Figure 1

Distance Traveled at Different Average Speeds

Time (hr)	Distance for Speed of 50 mi/h	Distance for Speed of 55 mi/h	Distance for Speed of 60 mi/h
0	0	0	0
1	50	55	60
2	100	110	120
3	150	165	180
4	200	220	240
5	250	275	300
6	300	330	360

Writing More Equations

Goals

- Write two-step equations to represent relationships between variables and describe how the pattern of change shows up in a table, a graph, or an equation

- Use tables, graphs, and equations to answer questions

All of the equations in Problem 3.1 involved only one arithmetic operation, namely multiplication. This problem builds on Problem 3.2 by presenting relationships whose equations involve two arithmetic operations. The reasoning process used to write the equations is the same.

Launch 3.2

Describe the context of the problem, which discusses group admission prices for Wild World. Make sure students understand how the pricing works: the park charges a fixed fee of $50 plus $10 per group member. The $50 fee is the same no matter what size the group is.

Suggested Questions

- *Think back to the last problem. Say a van is traveling at 50 miles per hour. How do you find the distance traveled in 3 hours?* (Multiply 50 times 3.)

- *So you only needed to use one operation, multiplication.*

- *Now think about the group-admission price. What calculations do you need to do to find the admission price for a group of 8 people?* (Multiply 8 by 10 and then add 50.)

- *So, for this situation, you need to use two operations, multiplication and addition.*

Tell students that they will be writing an equation for the relationship between the number of people in the group and the admission price. They will also write two-operations equations for other situations. Explain that they can use the same strategies that helped them write their equations in the last problem.

When you feel students understand what the challenge is, let them work in small groups on the problem, but require each student to write the answers and to be sure they can explain why their equations and answers are sensible. You may want to stop and have a class discussion after Question A to make sure students are having success writing two-operation equations before they move on to the other questions.

Explore 3.2

Suggested Questions As you walk around, ask students questions to help you better understand their thinking and recognize difficulties they may be having. For example, for Question A, you might ask the following:

- *What are the variables involved in the relationship?* (number of people in the group, admission price)

- *Which letters stand for the variables?* (n is the number of people and p is the price.)

- *Which is the dependent variable and which is the independent variable? Why?* (The price depends on the number of group members, so price is the dependent variable and number of people is the independent variable.)

- *How do you find the price for a given number of people?* (Start with $50 and add $10 times the number of people.)

- *How could you show this in an equation?* ($p = 50 + 10n$ or $p = 10n + 50$)

- *Show me how you would use your equation to find the price for 25 people. Which operation do you do first?* (Substitute 25 for n to get $p = 50 + 10 \times 25$. Multiply 10 and 25, and then add 50.)

Students who are thinking about the situation will know to multiply before adding. However, some students who look at $50 + 10 \times 25$ without thinking about the context, may add first. Remind students that the order of operations states that multiplication is done before addition or use the context to help students make sense of the order of operations.

INVESTIGATION 3

You might ask some groups to put their graphs and tables on transparencies to share during the summary.

Summarize 3.2

Have students share their equations, tables, graphs, and reasoning. Many of the questions you asked as you visited groups during the Explore are also appropriate in the summary.

Suggested Questions Ask questions such as the following during the discussion of Question B.

- *How is the equation for the bonus-card points similar to the equation for the admission price? How is it different?* (Both equations involve two operations. In the admission-price equation, you multiply and then add. In the bonus-card equation, you multiply and then subtract.

- *How are the graphs for the bonus-card points and the admission price alike and different? What are the reasons for the similarities and differences?* (Both graphs are straight lines, indicating that the change is constant. The graph for admission price slants up because the price increases by a constant amount for each person. The graph for the bonus card slants down because the number of points decreases with each ride.)

- *The graphs for time and distance in the last problem all went through the point (0, 0). Do these graphs go through (0, 0)? Why or why not?* (No. The "starting value" for the admission price is $50. If 0 people are in the group, the price is $50, not $0. The "starting value" for the bonus card is 100 points. If you take 0 rides, you have 100 points, not 0 points.)

- *How do the patterns of change show up in the table, graph, and equation?* (In the table, as the number of rides r increases by one, the points on the card decrease by six. In the graph, the line slants downward from (0, 100) going over one and down six from one point to the next. In the equation, the loss of six points is shown in the $-6r$.)

During the discussion of Question C, you might ask

- *How does this equation compare to the equations you wrote for Questions A and B?* (All three involve two operations, but the numbers in the equations are different. This equation is more like the equation in Question A because you multiply and then add.

- *How does this graph compare to the graphs you made in Questions A and B?* (All three involve graphs that are straight lines. This one slants up like the graph in Question A.)

3.2 Writing More Equations

Mathematical Goals

- Write two-step equations to represent relationships between variables and describe how the pattern of change shows up in a table, graph, or equation
- Use tables, graphs, and equations to answer questions

Launch

Describe the context of the problem.

Help students note that each equation in Problem 3.1 involved only one operation, multiplication. Ask students to find the admission price for a group of 8. Point out that they did two operations, multiplication and addition. Tell students that they will be writing equations for this and other relationships involving two operations.

Explore

Ask:

- *What are the variables involved in the relationship? Which is the dependent variable and which is the independent variable?*
- *How do you find the price for a given number of people? How could you show this in an equation?*
- *Show me how you would use your equation to find the price for 25 people. Which operation do you do first?*

Materials
- Transparent Grids

Summarize

Have students share their solutions. For Question B, ask:

- *How is the equation for the bonus-card points similar to the equation for the admission price? How is it different?*
- *How are the graphs for the bonus-card points and the admission price alike and different? What are the reasons for the similarities and differences?*
- *The graphs for time and distance in the last problem all went through the point (0, 0). Do the graphs go through (0, 0)? Why or why not?*

For Question C, ask:

- *How does this equation (graph) compare to the equations (graphs) you wrote for Questions A and B?*

Materials
- Student notebooks
- Transparency 3.2

ACE Assignment Guide for Problem 3.2

Differentiated Instruction
Solutions for All Learners

ore 5–8

ther *Applications* 9–12, *Connections* 28–37, xtensions 44–47; unassigned choices from earlier roblems

Adapted For suggestions about adapting ACE exercises, see the *CMP Special Needs Handbook*.
Connecting to Prior Units 28–32, 37: *Covering and Surrounding*; 33: *Data About Us*; 35: *Shapes and Designs*; 36: *Prime Time*

Answers to Problem 3.2

A. 1. $250; $400; $470

2. Multiply the number of people in the group by $10 and add $50.

3. $p = 50 + 10n$

4.

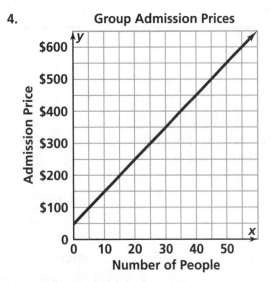

Group Admission Prices

5. The constant increase of $10 per person is shown as the 10 in the $10n$ part of the equation. In the graph, it is shown by the upward-slanting straight line. As n increases by 1 (horizontal distance), p increases by 10 (vertical distance). If $p = 50 + 10n$ is graphed on the same axes as the graphs in Problem 3.1, it would be less steep than the other graphs.

B. 1.

Bonus-Card Balance

Number in Rides	0	1	2	3	5	7	10	13	16
Points on Card	100	94	88	82	70	58	40	22	4

2. To find the number of points left, multiply the number of rides taken by 6 and subtract the product from 100.

3. $p = 100 - 6r$, where p is the number of points left after r rides

4.

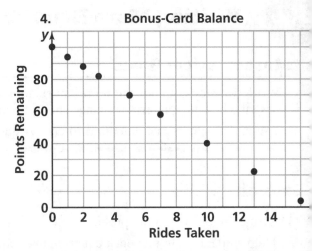

Bonus-Card Balance

5. The constant decreasing pattern is shown in the graph by a line that slants downward. It is shown in the equation by the fact that $6r$ is subtracted from 100. Each time r increases by 1, 6 more points are subtracted from 100, giving a smaller and smaller value of p. The pattern is similar in A in that the graphs of both A and B are lines. The pattern in A increases as n increases while the pattern in B decreases as r increases.

C. 1. c is the rental cost, h is the number of hours the cart is rented, 20 is a fixed fee of $20, and 5 is the dollar amount the rental costs increases by each hour.

2.

Cart Rental Costs

Number of Hours	1	2	3	4	5	6
Rental Cost	$25	$30	$35	$40	$45	$50

3.

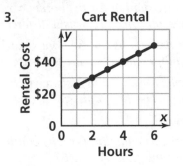

Cart Rental

4. The constant increasing pattern is shown in the graph by a line that slants upward. It is shown in the equation by the fact that $5h$ is added to 10. Each time h increases by 1, 5 more dollars are added to 20, giving a larger and larger value of c.

Paying Bills and Counting Profits

Goal

• Write equations to represent situations

In this problem, students write equations for calculating revenue, expenses, and profits for Ocean Bike Tours based on the number of customers. They also adjust the equation to account for new information.

Launch 3.3

Use the story of the bike trip and the need to make money as a way to get students thinking about the ideas of revenue, expenses, and profit.

Suggested Questions Have students look at Sidney's table. Ask questions to make sure they understand what the table shows.

• *The* revenue *is the money a company takes in. For Ocean Bike Tours, it is the money customers pay. Does the revenue depend on the number of customers?* (yes) *How much revenue does the company make per customer?* ($350)

• *The* expenses *are the things the company has to spend money for. What expenses are shown in this table?* (bike rental and food and camp costs)

• *Do these expenses depend on the number of customers?* (yes) *What is the total of all the expenses for each customer?* ($30 + $125 = $155)

• *The* profit *is the money a company makes after all the expenses are paid. How would you calculate the profit for the tour?* (Subtract the expenses from the revenue.)

• *Based on this table, will Ocean Bike Tours make a profit if they have only one customer?* (yes) *How much profit will they make?* ($350 − $155 = $195)

When you feel that students understand the table and the meanings of revenue, profit, and expenses, let them work on the problem in pairs or small groups.

Explore 3.3

Check to be sure students are correctly filling in their tables. For students to find the appropriate patterns, it is essential that the values be correct. Students should discuss their computations with other members of their groups. Sharing computation methods and putting these ideas into words will help all the students in a group. Encourage group members to compare and check the final table entries to make sure everyone has the correct information.

The relationships in the table are linear; that is, the rate of change is constant. Students might not recognize these as linear because the information is in a table instead of a graph. (Linear relationships are discussed in a later unit.)

Some students may have trouble with Question D because, unlike the other expenses, the cost for the van does not depend on the number of customers. Encourage students to consider specific cases before thinking about the general rules. For example, ask them what the expenses and profits would be for 5, 10, and 15 customers.

This data is rich with possibilities for additional rule writing, so you might want students to keep the table so you can return to these situations as you explore symbolic rules further.

Ask some groups to put their tables on Transparency 3.3 or chart paper.

Summarize 3.3

Suggested Questions Display Transparency 3.3. Ask:

• *How did you fill in the revenue column?* (Write their rule in words.)

• *What are the variables?* (Underline them in the rule.)

• *How did you to translate the rule into an equation?*

Repeat these questions for the bike rental, food and camp costs, and total expenses columns. Ask students how they can find the total expenses for any number of customers. Make sure both of these possibilities are mentioned:

- Multiply $30 by the number of customers, and multiply $125 by the number of customers. Then, add the two results.

- Add $30 and $125, and multiply the sum, $155, by the number of customers.

Translate both versions of the rule into equations.

Repeat this process for the profit column. There are several correct versions of the profit equation, including $p = 350n - 155n$,
$p = 350n - (30n + 125n)$,
$p = 350n - 30n - 125n$, and $p = 195n$. Allow all the variations students came up with to be presented. Students do not yet have the algebraic skills to prove that these equations are equivalent, but they can convince themselves of the equivalence by showing the equations give the same results for a few different n values. (If someone suggests $p = 350n - 30n + 125n$, help them see why this is wrong: This equation subtracts the bike rental expenses from the revenue and then *adds* the camp and food expenses. This is clearly incorrect.)

Discuss the answers to Question C. These answers are found most easily by substituting the given number of customers into the appropriate equation.

Suggested Questions For Question D, ask:

- *What is the van-rental cost if 5 people go on the tour? If 10 people go? If 25 people go?* (It is $700 no matter how many people go, up to a point. For this problem, assume they only need one van.)

- *Is the van-rental cost a variable? Why or why not?* (No. It is not a variable because it doesn't change.)

- *How can you change your equation for expenses to account for the van?* (add 700 to the right side) *What is the new equation?* (Possible equation: $e = 155n + 700$)

- *What would the new profit equation be?* (Possible equations: $p = 350n - (155n + 700$ or $p = 350n - 155n - 700$)

There are several correct variations of the expense and profit equations. As before, students can check the equivalence of different forms by evaluating the equations for several values of n.

Have students use the new equations to find the expenses and profits for a few different numbers of customers. Ask them how many customers the company would need to earn a profit. For 1, 2, and 3 customers, the profit is negative, which indicates the company will lose money. Students will probably be able to calculate the negative amounts with their calculators, but they may not completely understand what these numbers mean. Don't worry about this now. Students will come back to these ideas in *Accentuate the Negative*, a unit on integers.

Check for Understanding

- *The students decide to give each of the riders a T-shirt with Ocean Bike Tours on it. The shirts cost $6 each. What would the profit be if 20 customers go on the tour? Explain how you calculated your answer.* ($3,080; Possible explanation: If you include the T-shirts, the profit equation becomes $p = 350n - (155n + 700 + 6n)$. Substituting 20 for n gives $p = 3,080$.)

3.3 Paying Bills and Counting Profits

Mathematical Goal

• Write equations to represent situations

Launch

Discuss the table and the ideas of revenue, expenses, and profit.

• *The* revenue *is the money a company takes in. For Ocean Bike Tours, it is the money customers pay. Does the revenue depend on the number of customers? How much revenue does the company make per customer?*

• *The* expenses *are the things the company has to spend money for. What expenses are shown in this table? Do these expenses depend on the number of customers? What is the total of all the expenses for each customer?*

• *The* profit *is the money a company makes after all the expenses are paid. How would you calculate the profit for the tour?*

• *Based on this table, will Ocean Bike Tours make a profit if they have only one customer? If so, how much profit will they make?*

Have students work in pairs or small groups.

Materials
• Transparency 3.3 (optional)

Explore

Check that students are correctly filling in their tables. Have group members discuss computation methods and check each other's results.

If students have trouble with Question D, encourage them to consider specific cases before thinking about the general rules.

Summarize

Have a student fill in the revenue column. Have students help you write the rule for finding revenue in words and then translate it into an equation. Repeat this process for total expenses and profit. Accept all correct forms of the equations for expenses and profit. Students can verify that forms are equivalent by checking them for a few *n* values.

Discuss the answers to Questions C and D. For Question D, ask:

• *What is the van-rental cost if 5 people go on the tour? If 10 people go? If 25 people go? Is the van-rental cost a variable?*

• *How can you change your equation for expenses to account for the van? What would the new profit equation be?*

Have students use the new equations to find the expenses and profits for a few different numbers of customers. Ask them how many customers the company would need to have a profit. For 1, 2, and 3 customers, the profit is negative, which indicates the company will lose money. Students will explore negative numbers in the unit *Accentuate the Negative.*

Materials
• Student notebooks

ACE Assignment Guide for Problem 3.3

Core 13–19

Other *Applications* 20; *Connections* 38–42;
Extensions 48, 49; unassigned choices from earlier
problems

Adapted For suggestions about adapting
ACE exercises, see the *CMP Special Needs
Handbook.*
Connecting to Prior Units 38, 39: *Bits and Pieces II*

Answers to Problem 3.3

A. (Figure 2)

B. 1. $r = 350n$

   2. $e = 155n$, or $e = 30n + 125n$

   3. $p = 350n - 155n$, or
      $p = 350n - (30n + 125n)$, or $p = 195n$

C. For 20 customers, revenue is $7,000, expenses
are $3,100, and profit is $3,900.
For 31 customers, revenue is $10,850, expenses
are $4,805, and profit is $6,045.

D. 1. The constant 700 would be added to the
expression for expenses, so the equation
would become $e = 155n + 700$, or
$e = 30n + 125n + 700$

   2. The constant 700 would have to be
subtracted, so the equation would become
$p = 350n - 155n - 700$. (There are many
other possible correct equations that are
equivalent to this one.)

Figure 2

Tour Revenue and Expenses

Number of Customers	Revenue	Bike Rental	Food and Camp Costs	Total Expense	Profit
1	$350	$30	$125	$155	$195
2	$700	$60	$250	$310	$390
3	$1,050	$90	$375	$465	$585
4	$1,400	$120	$500	$620	$780
5	$1,750	$150	$625	$775	$975
6	$2,100	$180	$750	$930	$1,170

Investigation 3

Rules and Equations

In the last investigation, you used tables and graphs of relationships to find values of one variable for given values of the other variable. In some cases, you could only estimate or predict a value.

For some relationships, you can write an equation, or formula, to show how the variables are related. Using an equation is often the most accurate way to find values of a variable.

In this investigation, you will use the patterns in tables to help you write equations for relationships. You will then use your equations to compute values of the dependent variable for specific values of the independent variable.

3.1 Writing Equations

On the last day of the Ocean Bike Tour, the riders will be near Wild World Amusement Park. Liz and Malcolm want to plan a stop there. They consider several variables that affect their costs and the time they can spend at Wild World.

Getting Ready for Problem 3.1

- What variables do you think are involved in planning for the amusement-park trip?

- How are those variables related to each other?

Investigation 3 Rules and Equations **49**

STUDENT PAGE

STUDENT PAGE

Notes _____

_____

_____

_____

(49) 80

Malcolm finds out that it costs $21 per person to visit Wild World. Liz suggests they make a table or graph relating admission price to the number of people. However, Malcolm says there is a simple **rule** for calculating the cost:

The *cost* in dollars is equal to 21 times the *number of people*.

He writes the rule as an **equation**:

cost = 21 × *number of people*

Liz shortens Malcolm's equation by using single letters to stand for the variables. She uses *c* to stand for the cost and *n* to stand for the number of people:

$c = 21 \times n$

When you multiply a number by a letter variable, you can leave out the multiplication sign. So, 21*n* means 21 × *n*. You can shorten the equation even more:

$c = 21n$

The equation $c = 21n$ involves one calculation. You multiply the number of customers *n* by the cost per customer $21. Many common equations involve one calculation.

Problem 3.1 Equations With One Operation

The riders visited Wild World and the tour is over. They put their bikes and gear into vans and head back to Atlantic City, 320 miles away. On their way back, they try to calculate how long the drive home will take. They use a table and a graph to estimate their travel time for different average speeds.

A. Copy and complete the table.

Distance Traveled at Different Average Speeds

Time (hr)	Distance for Speed of 50 mi/h	Distance for Speed of 55 mi/h	Distance for Speed of 60 mi/h
0	0	■	■
1	50	■	■
2	100	■	■
3	■	■	■
4	■	■	■
5	■	■	■
6	■	■	■

50   Variables and Patterns

Notes _____

_____

_____

_____

B. Copy and complete the graph for all three speeds below. Use a different color for each speed.

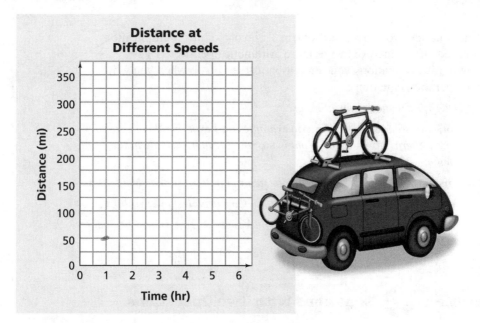

Distance at Different Speeds

C. Do the following for each of the three average speeds:

    1. Look for patterns relating distance and time in the table and graph. Write a rule in words for calculating the distance traveled in any given time.

    2. Write an equation for your rule, using letters to represent the variables.

    3. Describe how the pattern of change shows up in the table, graph, and equation.

D. For each speed, (50, 55, and 60 mph) tell how far you would travel in the given time. Explain how you can find each answer by using the table, the graph, and the equation.

    1. 3 hours   **2.** $4\frac{1}{2}$ hours   **3.** $5\frac{1}{4}$ hours

E. For each speed, find how much time it will take the students to reach these cities on their route:

    1. Atlantic City, New Jersey, about 320 miles from Norfolk

    2. Baltimore, Maryland, about $\frac{3}{4}$ of the way from Norfolk to Atlantic City

ACE **Homework starts on page 55.**

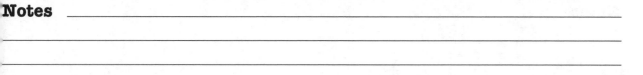

STUDENT PAGE

Notes

3.2 Writing More Equations

The equations you wrote in Problem 3.1 involved only multiplication. Some equations involve two or more arithmetic operations ($+, -, \times, \div$). To write such equations, you can reason just as you do when you write one-operation equations:

Determine what the variables are.

Work out some specific numeric examples and examine them carefully. What patterns do you see? What is the role of each variable in the calculation?

Write a rule in words to describe the general pattern in the calculations.

Convert your rule to an equation with letter variables and symbols.

Think about whether your equation makes sense. Test it for a few values to see if it works.

Problem 3.2 Equations With Two Operations

When Liz tells Theo about the idea to visit Wild World, he suggests she check to see whether the park offers special prices for large groups. She finds this information on the park's Web site:

A. 1. Find the price of admission for a group of 20 people, a group of 35 people, and a group of 42 people.

2. Describe in words how you can calculate the admission price for a group with any number of people.

Notes _____

_____

_____

_____

3. Write an equation for the admission price p for a group of n people.

4. Sketch a graph to show the admission price for a group of any size.

5. How does the pattern of change show up in the equation and graph? How is this pattern similar to the pattern in Problem 3.1? How is it different?

B. Admission to Wild World includes a bonus card with 100 points that can be spent on rides. Rides cost 6 points each.

1. Copy and complete the table below to show a customer's bonus card balance after each ride. Pay close attention to the values in the Number of Rides row.

Bonus Card Balance

Number of Rides	0	1	2	3	5	7	10	13	16
Points on Card	100	■	■	■	■	■	■	■	■

2. Describe in words how you can calculate the number of points left after any number of rides.

3. Write an equation showing the relation between the number of rides and the points left on the bonus card. Use letters to represent the variables.

4. Sketch a graph of the data.

5. How does the pattern of change between the variables show up in the equation and graph? How is this pattern similar to the pattern in Question A? How is it different?

C. Liz wonders whether they should rent a golf cart to carry the riders' backpacks at the park. The equation $c = 20 + 5h$ shows the cost c in dollars of renting a cart for h hours:

1. Explain what information the numbers and variables in the equation represent.

2. Use the equation to make a table for the cost of renting a cart for 1, 2, 3, 4, 5, and 6 hours.

3. Make a graph of the data.

4. Describe how the pattern of change between the two variables shows up in the table, graph, and equation.

ACE Homework starts on page 55.

Notes _____

_____

_____

_____

_____

3.3 Paying Bills and Counting Profits

The students think that $350 is a fair price to charge for the tour. Sidney wants to be certain Ocean Bike Tours will make a profit if they charge $350. She starts making the table below.

Tour Revenue and Expenses

Number of Customers	Revenue	Bike Rental	Food and Camp Costs	Total Expenses	Profit
1	$350	$30	$ 125		
2	$700	$60	$250		
3	$1,050	$90	$375		

Problem 3.3 Equations for Revenue, Expenses, and Profit

A. Extend and complete Sidney's table for 1 to 6 customers.

B. Write a rule in words and an equation for calculating the

   1. revenue r for n customers

   2. total expenses e for n customers

   3. profit p for n customers

C. Use the equations you wrote in Question B to find the revenue, expenses, and profit for 20 customers and for 31 customers.

D. Sidney forgot that the tour operators need to rent a van to carry equipment. The rental cost for the van will be $700.

   1. How does this expense affect the equation for total expenses?

   2. How does this expense affect the equation for profit?

ACE Homework starts on page 55.

Notes

_____

_____

_____

_____

Applications

1. The El Paso Middle School girls' basketball team is going from El Paso to San Antonio for the Texas state championship game. The trip will be 560 miles. Their bus travels at an average speed of 60 miles per hour.

a. Suppose the bus travels at an almost steady speed throughout the trip. Make a table and a graph of time and distance data for the bus.

b. Estimate the distance the bus travels in 2 hours, $2\frac{3}{4}$ hours, $3\frac{1}{2}$ hours, and 7.25 hours.

c. How are 2 hours and the distance traveled in 2 hours represented in the table? How are they shown on the graph?

d. How are $2\frac{3}{4}$ hours and the distance traveled in $2\frac{3}{4}$ hours represented in the table? How are they shown on the graph?

e. Describe in words a rule you can use to calculate the distance traveled for any given time on this trip.

f. The bus route passes through Sierra Blanca, which is 90 miles from El Paso. About how long does it take the bus to get to Sierra Blanca?

g. The bus route also passes through Balmorhea, which is $\frac{1}{3}$ of the way from El Paso to San Antonio. About how long does it take the bus to get to Balmorhea?

h. How long does it take the bus to complete its 560-mile trip to San Antonio?

Investigation 3 Rules and Equations **55**

Notes _____

_____

_____

_____

2. Celia writes the equation $d = 8t$ to represent the distance in miles d that bikers could travel in t hours at a speed of 8 miles per hour.

   a. Make a table that shows the distance traveled every half hour, up to 5 hours, if bikers ride at this constant speed.

   b. How far would bikers travel in 1 hour, 6 hours, 8.5 hours, and 10 hours?

3. The equation $d = 70t$ represents the distance in miles covered after traveling at 70 miles per hour for t hours.

   a. Make a table that shows the distance traveled every half hour from 0 hours to 4 hours.

   b. Sketch a coordinate graph that shows the distance traveled between 0 and 4 hours.

   c. What is d when $t = 2.5$ hours?

   d. What is t when $d = 210$ miles?

   e. You probably made your graph by plotting points. In this situation, would it make sense to connect these points?

4. a. Use the table to write an equation that relates lunch cost L and number of riders n.

Bike Tour Box Lunch Costs

Riders	1	2	3	4	5	6	7	8	9
Lunch Cost	$4.25	$8.50	$12.75	$17.00	$21.25	$25.50	$29.75	$34.00	$38.25

   b. Use your equation to find the lunch cost for 25 riders.

   c. How many riders could eat lunch for $89.25?

For Exercises 5–7, use the equation to complete the table.

5. $y = 4x + 3$

x	1	2	5	10	20
y	▦	▦	▦	▦	▦

6. $m = 100 - k$

k	1	2	5	10	20
m	▦	▦	▦	▦	▦

7. $d = 3.5t$

t	1	2	5	10	20
d	▦	▦	▦	▦	▦

56 Variables and Patterns

Notes _____

_____

_____

_____

8. Sean is buying a new DVD player and speakers for $315. The store offers him an interest-free payment plan that allows him to pay in monthly installments of $25.

    a. How much will Sean still owe after one payment? After two payments? After three payments?

    b. Use n to stand for the number of payments and a for the amount still owed. Write an equation for calculating a for any value of n.

    c. Use your equation to make a table and a graph showing the relationship between n and a.

    d. As n increases by 1, how does a change? How is this change shown in the table? How is it shown on the graph?

    e. How many payments will Sean have to make in all? How is this shown in the table? How is this shown on the graph?

For Exercises 9–12, express each rule as an equation. Use single letters to stand for the variables. Identify what each letter represents.

  9. The area of a rectangle is its length multiplied by its width.

 10. The number of hot dogs needed for the picnic is two for each student.

 11. The amount of material needed to make the curtains is 4 square yards per window.

 12. Taxi fare is $2.00 plus $1.10 per mile.

 13. The sales tax in a state is 8%. Write an equation for the amount of tax t on an item that costs p dollars.

 14. An airplane is traveling at 550 miles per hour. Write an equation for the distance d the plane travels in h hours.

 15. Potatoes sell for $0.25 per pound at the produce market. Write an equation for the cost c of p pounds of potatoes.

 16. A cellular family phone plan costs $49 per month plus $0.05 per minute of long-distance service. Write an equation for the monthly bill b when m minutes of long-distance service are used.

Investigation 3 Rules and Equations   **57**

STUDENT PAGE

Notes _____

_____

_____

_____

Applications

STUDENT PAGE

(57) 80

For Exercises 17–19, describe the relationship between the variables in words and with an equation.

17.

x	1	2	5	10	20
y	4	8	20	40	80

Homework
Help Online
PHSchool.com
For: Help with Exercise 17
Web Code: ane-1317

18.

s	1	2	3	6	12
t	49	48	47	44	38

19.

n	1	2	3	4	5
z	6	11	16	21	26

20. **Multiple Choice** Which equation describes the relationship in the table?

n	0	1	2	3	4	5	6
C	10	20	30	40	50	60	70

A. $C = 10n$ **B.** $C = 10 + n$ **C.** $C = 10$ **D.** $C = 10 + 10n$

Connections

21. The perimeter P of a square is related to the side length s by the formula $P = 4s$. The area, A, is related to the side length by the formula $A = s \times s$, or $A = s^2$.

   a. Make a table showing how the perimeter of a square increases as the side length increases from 1 to 6 in 1-unit steps. Describe the pattern of change.

   b. Make a table showing how the area of a square increases as the side length increases from 1 to 6. Describe the pattern of change.

$$s$$
$$P = 4s$$
$$A = s^2$$

For Exercises 22–27, find the indicated value or values.

22. the mean, or average, of 4.5 and 7.3

23. the area of a circle with radius 6 centimeters

24. the sum of the angle measures in a triangle, in a parallelogram, in a pentagon, and in a hexagon

Go Online
PHSchool.com
For: Multiple-Choice Skills Practice
Web Code: ana-1354

STUDENT PAGE

Notes _____

_____

_____

_____

25. the 10th odd number (1 is the first odd number, 3 is the second odd number, and so on.)

26. the area of a triangle with a base of 10 centimeters and a height of 15 centimeters

27. $3^3 \times 5^2 \times 7$

28. The wheels on Kai's bike are 27 inches in diameter. His little sister, Masako, has a bike with wheels that are 20 inches in diameter. Kai and Masako are on a bike ride.

   a. How far does Kai go in one complete turn of his wheels?

   b. How far does Masako go in one complete turn of her wheels?

   c. How far does Kai go in 500 turns of his wheels?

   d. How far does Masako go in 500 turns of her wheels?

   e. How many times do Kai's wheels have to turn to cover 100 feet?

   f. How many times do Masako's wheels have to turn to cover 100 feet? To cover 1 mile?

29. Bicycles that were popular in the 1890s were called "penny farthing" bicycles. These bikes had front wheels with diameters as great as 5 feet! Suppose the front wheel of these bicycles have a diameter of 5 feet.

   a. What is the radius of the front wheel?

   b. How far will one bike travel in 100 turns of the front wheel?

   c. How many times will the front wheel turn in a 3-mile trip?

   d. Compare the number of times the wheels of Masako's bike turn in a 1-mile trip [see part (f) of Exercise 28] with the number of times the front wheel of this penny-farthing bike turns in a 3-mile trip. Why are the numbers related this way?

Investigation 3 Rules and Equations   **59**

Notes _____

_____

_____

_____

Write a formula for the given quantity.

30. the area A of a rectangle with length l and width w

31. the area A of a parallelogram with base b and height h

32. the perimeter P of a rectangle with base b and height h

33. the mean m of two numbers p and q

34. the area A of a circle with radius r

35. the sum S of the measures of angles in a polygon of n sides

36. the nth odd number, O (1 is the first odd number, 3 is the second odd number, and so on.)

37. the area A of a triangle with base b and height h

Complete the table of values for the given equation.

38. $y = x + \frac{1}{2}$

x	$\frac{1}{5}$	$\frac{1}{4}$	$\frac{1}{3}$	$\frac{2}{5}$	$\frac{1}{2}$	$\frac{2}{3}$	$\frac{3}{4}$	5
y	■	■	■	■	■	■	■	■

39. $y = \left(\frac{1}{2}\right)x$

x	$\frac{1}{5}$	$\frac{1}{4}$	$\frac{1}{3}$	$\frac{2}{5}$	$\frac{1}{2}$	$\frac{2}{3}$	$\frac{3}{4}$	5
y	■	■	■	■	■	■	■	■

Describe the relationship between x and y in words.

40.

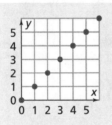

41.

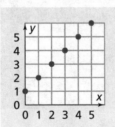

42.

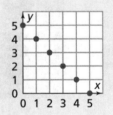

Notes _____

_____

_____

_____

Extensions

43. a. You can calculate the average speed of a car trip if you know the distance and time traveled. Copy and complete the table below.

Car Trips

Distance (mi)	Time (hr)	Average Speed (mi/h)
145	2	■
110	2	■
165	2.5	■
300	5.25	■
446	6.75	■
528	8	■
862	9.5	■
723	10	■

b. Write a formula for calculating the average speed s for any given distance d and time t.

For Exercises 44–47, solve each problem by estimating and checking.

44. The equation $p = 50 + 10n$ gives the admission price p to Wild World for a group of n people. A club's budget has $500 set aside for a visit to the park. How many club members can go?

45. The equation $b = 100 - 6r$ gives the number of bonus points b left on a Wild World bonus card after r rides.

a. Rosi has 34 points left. How many rides has she been on?

b. Dwight has 16 points left. How many rides has he been on?

46. The equation $d = 2.5t$ describes the distance in meters d covered by a canoe-racing team in t seconds. How long does it take the team to go 125 meters? How long does it take them to go 400 meters?

47. The equation $d = 400 - 2.5t$ describes the distance in meters d of a canoe-racing team from the finish line t seconds after a race starts. When is the team 175 meters from the finish line? When is it 100 meters from the finish line?

Notes _____

_____

_____

_____

48. Armen builds models from rods. When he builds bridges, he makes the sides using patterns of triangles like the ones below. The total number of rods depends on the number of rods along the bottom.

Rods along bottom = 3
Total number of rods = 11

Rods along bottom = 4
Total number of rods = 15

a. Copy and complete the table.

Rod Bridges

Rods Along the Bottom	1	2	3	4	5	6	7	8	9	10
Total Number of Rods	3	7	11	■	■	■	■	■	■	■

b. Write an equation relating the total number of rods t to the number of rods along the bottom b. Explain how the formula you write relates to the way Armen puts the rods together.

c. What do you know about the properties of triangles and rectangles that makes the design above better than the one below?

49. The students in Problem 3.3 decide to visit Wild World Amusement Park on the tour. They include the cost of this and the van in their revenue and expenses. How does this affect the equation for profit?

Notes _____

_____

_____

_____

Mathematical Reflections 3

In this investigation, you wrote equations to express relationships between variables. The following questions will help you summarize what you have learned.

Think about your answers to these questions. Discuss your ideas with other students and your teacher. Then write a summary of your findings in your notebook.

1. What decisions do you need to make when you write an equation to represent a relationship between variables?

2. In what ways are equations useful?

3. In this unit, you have represented relationships with tables, graphs, and equations. List some advantages and disadvantages of each of these representations.

Notes _____

_____

_____

_____

Investigation 3

ACE
Assignment Choices

Problem 3.1
Core 1–4
Other *Connections* 21–27, *Extensions* 43

Problem 3.2
Core 5–8
Other *Applications* 9–12, *Connections* 28–37, *Extensions* 44–47; unassigned choices from previous problems

Problem 3.3
Core 13–19
Other *Applications* 20; *Connections* 38–42; *Extensions* 48, 49; unassigned choices from previous problems

Adapted For suggestions about adapting ACE exercises, see the CMP *Special Needs Handbook*.

Connecting to Prior Units Units 21, 23, 26, 28–32, 37: *Covering and Surrounding*; 22, 33: *Data About Us*; 24, 35: *Shapes and Designs*; 25, 27, 36: *Prime Time*; 38, 39: *Bits and Pieces II*

Applications

1. a.   **Basketball Road Trip**

Time (hr)	Distance (mi)
0	0
1	60
2	120
3	180
4	240
5	300
6	360
7	420
8	480
9	540
10	600

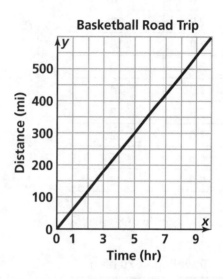

Basketball Road Trip

b. Estimates should be close to the following: 120 mi, 165 mi, 210 mi, 435 mi

c. The data are represented in the table by corresponding *x* and *y* values 2 and 120. They are represented by point (2, 120) on the graph.

d. These values are not in the table. They would be the values $\frac{3}{4}$ of the way between (2, 120) and (3, 180). If the plotted points on the graph are connected, then the values are represented by the point (2.75, 165) on the line.

e. The distance (in miles) is 60 multiplied by the time (in hours).

f. $1\frac{1}{2}$ hours

g. about 3 hours 7 minutes; $\frac{1}{3}$ of 560 mi is about 187 mi

h. $9\frac{1}{3}$ hours, or 9 hours 20 minutes

2. a.

Bike Ride

Time (hr)	Distance (mi)
0	0
0.5	4
1.0	8
1.5	12
2.0	16
2.5	20
3.0	24
3.5	28
4.0	32
4.5	36
5.0	40

b. 8 miles; 48 miles; 68 miles; 80 miles

3. a.

Traveling at 70 mph

Time (hr)	Distance (mi)
0	0
0.5	35
1.0	70
1.5	105
2.0	140
2.5	175
3.0	210
3.5	245
4.0	280

b.

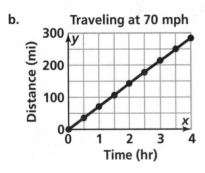

Traveling at 70 mph

c. $d = 175$ miles

d. $t = 3$ hours

e. Yes, in this case the information represented by a line connecting the points is accurate because the distance increases at a constant rate (so there would not be any jumps or curves between points).

4. a. $L = 4.25n$

b. $L = 4.25 \times 25 = \$106.25$

c. We need to find n so that $\$89.25 = 4.25n$. What number multiplied by 4.25 gives 89.25? $n = 21$ people

5.

x	1	2	5	10	20
y	7	11	23	43	83

6.

k	1	2	5	10	20
m	99	98	95	90	80

7.

t	1	2	5	10	20
d	3.5	7	17.5	35	70

8. a. \$290 after 1 payment; \$265 after 2 payments; \$240 after 3 payments

b. $a = 315 - 25n$

c. **Sean's Loan Payments**

Number of Months	Amount Owed
0	$315
1	$290
2	$265
3	$240
4	$215
5	$190
6	$165
7	$140
8	$115
9	$90
10	$65
11	$40
12	$15
13	−$10

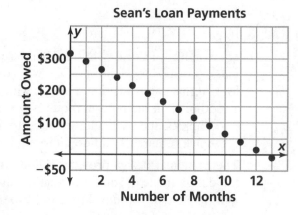

Sean's Loan Payments

d. As n increases by 1, a decreases by $25. As you read down the columns of the table, the amount owed decreases by $25 each time the number of months increases by 1. The points of the graph lie on a line that slants downward as you read from left to right. More specifically, if we move 1 unit to the right on the x-axis, the line moves downward 25 units on the y-axis.

e. Sean will pay off the loan in 13 months. His last payment will be only $15. In the table, the amount owed drops below 0 on month 13. In the graph, the point for $x = 13$ is below the x-axis.

9. $A = lw$, where A is the area, l is the length, and w is the width

10. $h = 2s$, where h is the number of hot dogs and s is the number of students

11. $y = 4w$, where y is the amount of material in yards and w is the number of windows

12. $t = 2 + 1.10m$, where t is the taxi fare in dollars and m is the number of miles

13. $t = 0.08p$ **14.** $d = 550h$

15. $c = 0.25p$ **16.** $b = 0.05m + 49$

17. y is 4 times x; $y = 4x$

18. t is 50 minus s; $t = 50 - s$

19. z is 1 more than 5 times n; $z = 5n + 1$

20. D

Connections

21. a.

Side (units)	1	2	3	4	5	6
Perimeter (units²)	4	8	12	16	20	24

The perimeter increases by 4 as the length of the side increases by 1.

b.

Side (units)	1	2	3	4	5	6
Area (units²)	1	4	9	16	25	36

The area is the square of the length of the side. It grows at an increasing rate as side length increases.

22. $\frac{(4.5 + 7.3)}{2} = 5.9$

23. $A = \pi 6^2 = 36\pi$ cm^2 ≈ 113.04

24. Triangle: 180°; parallelogram: 360°; pentagon: 540°; hexagon: 720°

25. 19

26. $A = \frac{1}{2} \times 10 \times 15 = 75$ cm^2

27. 4,725

28. a. Kai will travel 84.78 in. in one turn because the circumference of his wheel is about 3.14×27 in., or about 84.78 in.

b. Masako will travel about 62.8 in. for one turn because the circumference of her wheel is about 3.14×20 in., or 62.8 in.

c. Kai will travel about 42,390 in. for 500 turns because 84.78 × 500 = 42,390. Students may convert this to 3,532.5 ft or 1,177.5 yd.

d. Masako will travel about 31,400 in. for 500 turns because 62.8 × 500 = 31,400. Students may convert this to 2,617 ft or 872 yd.

e. 1,200 ÷ 84.78 ≈ 14.15 turns

f. 1,200 ÷ 62.8 ≈ 19.12 turns; 1 mi is 5,280 ft or 63,360 in. So, it would take 63,360 ÷ 62.8 ≈ 1,008.92 turns to cover 1 mi.

29. a. 2.5 ft

b. The bike will travel about 3.14 × 5 = 15.7 ft in one turn, so in 100 turns it will travel about 1,570 ft.

c. Because 3 mi = 15,840 ft, it will make 15,840 ÷ 15.7 ≈ 1,008.9 turns.

d. The big wheel can go three times as far for the same number of turns because its diameter is three times the diameter of Masako's wheel.

30. $A = lw$

31. $A = bh$

32. $P = 2b + 2h$ or $P = 2(b + h)$

33. $m = \dfrac{(p + q)}{2}$

34. $A = \pi r^2$

35. $S = (n - 2)180$

36. $O = 2n - 1$

37. $A = \frac{1}{2}bh$

38.

x	$\frac{1}{5}$	$\frac{1}{4}$	$\frac{1}{3}$	$\frac{2}{5}$	$\frac{1}{2}$	$\frac{2}{3}$	$\frac{3}{4}$	5
y	$\frac{7}{10}$	$\frac{3}{4}$	$\frac{5}{6}$	$\frac{9}{10}$	1	$\frac{7}{6}$	$\frac{5}{4}$	$\frac{11}{2}$

39.

x	$\frac{1}{5}$	$\frac{1}{4}$	$\frac{1}{3}$	$\frac{2}{5}$	$\frac{1}{2}$	$\frac{2}{3}$	$\frac{3}{4}$	5
y	$\frac{1}{10}$	$\frac{1}{8}$	$\frac{1}{6}$	$\frac{1}{5}$	$\frac{1}{4}$	$\frac{1}{3}$	$\frac{3}{8}$	$\frac{5}{2}$

40. y is equal to x

41. y is 1 more than x

42. y is 5 minus x

Extensions

43. a.

Speed for a Car Trip

Distance (mi)	Time (hr)	Average Speed (mi/h)
145	2	72.5
110	2	55
165	2.5	66
300	5.25	≈ 57.1
446	6.75	≈ 66.1
528	8	66
862	9.5	≈ 90.7
723	10	72.3

b. $s = \dfrac{d}{t}$

44. 45 club members

45. a. 11 rides

b. 14 rides

46. 50 seconds, 160 seconds

47. 90 seconds, 120 seconds

48. a. (Figure 3)

b. $t = 3 + 4(b - 1)$, or $t = 4b - 1$; There are many possible explanations. One way to look at this pattern is that a bridge with 1 toothpick on the bottom requires 3 toothpicks, and each additional bottom toothpick requires 4 additional toothpick

c. The triangular design provides rigidity tha the design made of squares doesn't. This i a principle that was developed in *Shapes and Designs* of Course 1.

49. Students need to subtract the cost of the amusement park from the tour profit with v found in Question D(2) of Problem 3.3. A way to approach this is to make a table usin

Figure 3   **Rod Bridges**

Rods Along Bottom	1	2	3	4	5	6	7	8	9	10
Total Number of Rods	3	7	11	15	19	23	27	31	35	39

columns 1 and 6 from the table made for Question A of Problem 3.3 and add two new columns. (Figure 4)

Reasoning symbolically:
Cost of Amusement park = $50 + 10n$;
Tour profit with van = $350n - 155n - 700$;
Tour profit with amusement park =
$350n - 155n - 700 - (50 + 10n) = 185n - 750$

This approach is more sophisticated and requires students to think about representing the subtraction of a quantity $(50 + 10n)$ from another quantity $350n - 155n - 700$.

Leaving the result as:
Tour profit with amusement park =
$350n - 155n - 700 - (50 + 10n)$ is fine at this point. In *Moving Straight Ahead* and *Say It With Symbols*, students will work more with writing and simplifying equations of this form.

Possible Answers to Mathematical Reflections

1. First, identify the variables involved in the relationship. Then, choose letters to stand for those variables. Deciding which variable is the dependent variable and which is the independent variable is helpful. Calculate some values of the dependent variable for specific values of the independent variable, and look for a pattern in those calculations. Describe the pattern in words. Finally, use the words as a guide to write an equation to represent the relationships.

2. Equations give you a short way to represent a relationship. They make calculating specific values more precise and efficient.

3. Tables allow you to see pairs of values. However, the number of pairs you can show in a table is limited. Also, it can be difficult to see the overall pattern in a table.

Graphs make it easy to see the overall pattern visually. However, it is harder to find exact values from a graph.

Equations provide a brief summary of the relationship and allow you to find values of one variable for any value of the other variable. Although you can tell some things about the overall pattern from an equation, it doesn't give a visual picture of the pattern.

Figure 4

Tour Revenue and Expenses

Number of Customers	Profit	Tour Profit With Van	Cost of Amusement Park	Profit With Van Minus Cost of Amusement Park
1	$195	−$505	$60	−$565
2	$390	−$310	$70	−$380
3	$585	−$115	$80	−$195
4	$780	$80	$90	−$10
5	$975	$275	$100	$175
6	$1,170	$470	$110	$360
n		$350n - 155n - 700$	$50 + 10n$	$185n - 750$
				$= 350n - 155n - 700 - (50 + 10n)$

Investigation 4 Calculator Tables and Graphs

Mathematical and Problem-Solving Goals

- Make and use graphing calculator tables
- Make and use graphing calculator graphs
- Use a graphing calculator to support problem solving

Summary of Problems

 Problem 4.1 **Making and Using Calculator Tables**

Students use their calculators to make tables for some of the situations they explored in the last investigation. They use the calculator tables to find interesting patterns, and to solve problems about values of both the independent and dependent variables.

Problem 4.2 **Making and Using Calculator Graphs**

Students graph equations on their calculators. They learn to adjust window settings and the axes scales, and to trace the graph to find coordinates of specific points. They use these skills to solve problems about Wild World amusement park.

Problem 4.3 **Extending the Tour**

Students compare price quotes for two bike rental companies. Students can solve the problem by using pencil and paper, by using a graphing calculator, or by using some combination of these two methods.

	Suggested Pacing	Materials for Students	Materials for Teachers	ACE Assignments
All	$4\frac{1}{2}$ days	Graphing calculators, student notebooks	Overhead graphing calculator (optional)	
4.1	$1\frac{1}{2}$ days		Transparency 4.1	1, 7–12
4.2	$1\frac{1}{2}$ days		Transparencies 4.2A, 4.2B, 4.2C	2–4, 13–17
4.3	1 day	Grid paper	Transparencies 4.3A and 4.3B	5, 6, 18, 19
MR	$\frac{1}{2}$ day			

Goal

Make and use graphing calculator tables

In this problem, students use graphing calculator tables to explore relationships between variables. We start with tables because many students are more comfortable working with tables than with graphs. The questions students are asked will be familiar, as they are similar to questions from previous investigations, but now students can use the capabilities of their graphing calculators to support their work.

Some students may have already used graphing calculators. Most students are interested in technology and will have few problems learning these calculator methods. You might have students who catch on quickly help others. An overhead display unit, if one is available, can help you to model the steps of making calculator tables (and to make graphs in the next investigation).

Launch 4.1

The student text has an introduction on how to enter an equation into a graphing calculator and make a graph. We use the formulas for circumference and area of a circle, which students encountered in the grade 6 unit *Covering and Surrounding*.

Suggested Questions To get a conversation started, ask students questions such as the following:

- *Who can tell us the formula for finding the circumference of a circle?*

Call on someone and ask the rest of the class if the person is correct. If the student says $C = \pi d$, say that the formula is correct, and then ask if anyone knows a formula that involves the radius, rather than the diameter. You are looking for the formula $C = 2\pi r$.

- *What are the variables in this formula?* (Circumference and radius. If some students say π, remind them that π stands for a specific number, which is approximately equal to 3.14. Because the value of π does not change, it is not a variable.)

- *Which is the dependent variable?* (circumference because it depends on the radius)

- *Who can tell us the formula for finding the area of a circle?* ($A = \pi r^2$)

- *What are the variables in this formula?* (area and radius)

- *Which is the dependent variable?* (area because it depends on the radius)

- *How are these formulas alike and how are they different?* (Possible responses: They both measure a circle in some way. They each have a constant of π and the radius of the circle as the independent variable.)

- *For which formula will the dependent variable grow faster as the radius increases? Why?* (area because you multiply π by the square of the radius for the area, but by only 2 times the radius for the circumference)

Write the formulas on the board for easy reference as you proceed. Explain to students that they will now learn how to use their graphing calculators to make tables of values for the formulas.

Use an overhead graphing calculator or the calculator screens on Transparency 4.1 or in the student book to guide students in entering the two equations and in setting up and displaying their tables.

Suggested Questions After students have successfully made their tables, use the Getting Ready questions to make sure they understand how to interpret them.

- *What does the number 28.274 in the third column mean?* (It is the area of a circle with a radius of 3 units.)

- *What does 25.133 in the second column mean?* (It is the circumference of a circle with a radius of 4 units.)

- *What does the 5 in the first column mean?* (It represents the radius of a circle.)

If necessary, ask about other values in the table. Show students how they can use the down arrow key to scroll down and see more values in the table.

If students have difficulty remembering which equation is in which column, show them that they can scroll upwards until the cursor is on Y_1 or Y_2 and the equation will appear at the bottom of the screen. Tell students that they will use their graphing calculator to solve problems about Wild World amusement park.

Have students work in groups on the problem. Students can help one another with using the calculators, but each student should enter the equations and make the tables on his or her own. (Note: A common ground rule teachers use is to allow students to help each other with the graphing calculator but only by giving verbal instructions. This way a student will learn the keystrokes needed.)

Explore 4.1

Have students set up and display calculator tables for each situation. As you walk around, you may need to help students adjust their table setups.

If a group is having trouble getting started, determine whether the difficulty is caused by the calculator or by the problem. You may need to demonstrate entering equations and setting up tables again for individual groups. Be sure students understand how to set the interval between x-values.

Summarize 4.1

Suggested Questions Have students share their answers and justifications. Ask questions such as:

- *What is the dependent variable? What is the independent variable?* (Admission price is the dependent variable. Number of customers is the independent variable.)

- *How can you find the admission price for a group of 26 people?* (Scroll down the table and find the y-value when $x = 26$.)

- *How can you find the number of people corresponding to an admission price of $480?* (Scroll down the table to find the x-value when $y = 480$. The x-value 43 corresponds to the y-value 480. 43 people can enter for $480.)

- *How did you find the answer to part (4) of Question A? How do you know that you are correct?* (Because 950 is the cost, you can scroll down the table to find an x-value that gives a y-value of 950. You can also subtract the 50 and divide by 10 to find that the cost for 90 customers is $950.)

After reviewing all the answers, choose a student to summarize how to use a table to find the value of the dependent variable for a given value of the independent variable. Then, have a different student explain how to find the value of the independent variable for a given value of the dependent variable.

- *Describe another method for finding the admission costs for 26 people.*

Check for Understanding

Have each student make a calculator table for the circumference formula for a circle. Students should work independently to answer these questions:

- *What is the value of the radius if the value of the circumference is approximately 75.398 cm* (12 cm)

- *What is the circumference of a circle with radius 7.5 cm?* (47.124 cm)

4.1 Making and Using Calculator Tables

Mathematical Goal

- Make and use graphing calculator tables

Launch

Introduce how to enter an equation or formula into a graphing calculator.

- *Who can tell us the formula for finding the circumference of a circle?*
- *What are the variables in this formula? Which is the dependent variable?*
- *Who can tell us the formula for finding the area of a circle?*
- *What are the variables in this formula? Which is the dependent variable?*
- *How are these formulas alike and how are they different?*
- *For which formula will the dependent variable grow faster as the radius increases? Why?*

Use an overhead graphing calculator or the drawings of the calculator screens on Transparency 4.1 or in the student book to guide students in entering the two equations and displaying the tables.

Discuss the Getting Ready questions.

Have students work in small groups.

Materials
- Graphing calculators
- Transparency 4.1
- Overhead graphing calculator (optional)

Explore

As you walk around, you may need to help students adjust their table setups. If a group is having trouble getting started, determine whether the difficulty is caused by the calculator or by the problem. Be sure students understand how to set the interval between *x*-values.

Materials
- Graphing calculator

Summarize

Have students share their answers and justifications. Ask questions such as:

- *What is the dependent variable? What is the independent variable?*
- *How can you find the admission price for a group of 26 people?*
- *How can you find the number of people corresponding to an admission price of $485?*
- *How did you find the answer to part (4) of Question A? How do you know that you are correct?*

Choose students to summarize how to use a table to find the value of the dependent variable for a given value of the independent variable and how to find the value of the independent variable for a given value of the dependent variable.

Materials
- Student notebooks
- Graphing calculators

continued on next page

continued

Check for Understanding

Have each student make a calculator table for the circumference formula for a circle.

- *What is the value of the radius if the value of the circumference is approximately 75.398?*
- *What is the circumference of a circle with radius 7.5 cm?*

ACE Assignment Guide for Problem 4.1

Differentiated Instruction
Solutions for All Learners

Core 1
Other *Connections* 7–12

Adapted For suggestions about adapting ACE exercises, see the *CMP Special Needs Handbook.*
Connecting to Prior Units 11: *Prime Time;* 12: *Bits and Pieces III*

Answers to Problem 4.1

A. 1. Check students' work.

X	Y1	
1	0	
2	60	
3	70	
4	80	
5	100	
6	110	
7	120	
X=1		

2. $310

3. 43

4. $n = 90$. If there are 90 people in the group, the price will be $950.

B. 1. Check students' work.

X	Y1	
4	10	
8	20	
12	30	
16	40	
20	50	
24	60	
28	70	
X=4		

2. 100 meters

3. $t = 175$. To travel 437.5 meters, the team must paddle for 175 seconds.

C. 1. Check students' work.

X	Y1	
0	100	
2	88	
4	76	
6	64	
8	52	
10	40	
12	28	
X=0		

2. The number of points decreases by 12, each time the number of rides increases by 2. That is because each ride costs 6 points, so two rides cost 12 points.

3. $r = 15$. After 15 rides, 10 points remain on a card.

Making and Using Calculator Graphs

Goal

• Make and use graphing calculator graphs

In this problem, students learn to make calculator graphs and to use them to explore relationships between variables and solve problems. It takes time and experience for students to understand what a graphic display can tell them. Students will make and interpret graphs throughout the rest of the curriculum.

Launch 4.2

Before making their first graph, have students follow the steps below. This will ensure that all students are looking at the same displays as you walk them through the steps of displaying a graph.

• Press MODE and make sure that everything on the left side of the screen is highlighted.

• Press Y= and delete any equations that are there.

• Press 2nd STAT PLOT . If any of the plots are on, press the number corresponding to the plot, and highlight "Off" on the screen that appears.

• To get a standard window display, press the ZOOM key and press 6.

Ask students to enter the equation $Y = 1.5X + 2$ into their calculators. Use the discussion in the student text to help students understand how to produce, adjust, and trace a graph on their calculators. Use an overhead graphing calculator to demonstrate or have students refer to Transparency 4.2A or the drawings of the calculator screens in their books.

Once students have entered the equation, have them press WINDOW to see the window settings. Discuss how the Xmin, Xmax, Ymin, Ymax, Xscl, and Yscl settings relate to the values on pencil-and-paper graphs. Explain that the settings shown are for the standard window. Have them press GRAPH to see the graph in the standard window.

Explain to students that sometimes they will want to look at a different part of the graph than that shown in the standard window. Have them adjust the settings as shown in the student book to show only values in the first quadrant, and then press GRAPH to see the graph.

Finally, have students press TRACE and then move the cursor along the graph. Ask what the values at the bottom of the screen mean.

Then use the Getting Ready and Transparency 4.2B to allow students to experiment with graphing on a graphing calculator. Emphasize that each set of the three graphs should be graphed on the same axes.

Let the class do this in pairs (or groups if you are confident that each student is actively engaged in the thinking process.) You might have each student think about the first problem and then move them into pairs (or groups) to discuss their strategies.

Suggested Questions After students have had time to experiment with the sets of equations, ask:

• *Which, if any, of the graphs show similar patterns of change? How are the graphs similar? How are the equations of the graphs similar?* (Possible answers: Set 1: The graphs show two straight lines that increase at the same rate. Both equations have a $3x$ and then a number added or subtracted. These lines appear to be parallel. Set 2: All the graphs are straight lines. Both $y = 3x$ and $y = 1x$ have a number times x with nothing else added or subtracted. Set 3: All three graphs are straight lines that increase from left to right, and all three equations have a number times x plus or minus a number. The graphs for the first two equations have the same rate of change. Both of these equations have a $2x$. They also look parallel. Set 4: The graphs of $y = 2x$ and $y = 2^x$ are both one piece, while the graph of $y = 2 \div x$ is two separate curves. The equations all have 2 and x in them.

• *How are the graphs different? How are the equations for the graphs different?* (Set 1: The graph of $y = x^2$ is a U-shaped curve, while the other graphs are lines. The equation is different from the others because x is squared and nothing is added or subtracted. The graphs of the two lines are different because they cross the y-axis in different places. The equations are different because one has a -4, and the other has a $+2$. Set 2: The graph of $y = 5$ is horizontal, while the other graphs are slanted. The equations for the slanted graphs have an x, while $y = 5$ doesn't. The slanted graphs have different rates of change. Their equations have different numbers in front of the x. Set 3: The graphs of the first two equations are different because they cross the y-axis in different places. The equations are different because the first has a $+3$ and the second has a -5. The third equation is different because it has a slower rate of change, it crosses the x-axis at a different place, and it has a $0.5x$ instead of a $2x$. Set 4: The graphs of $y = 2 \div x$ and $y = 2^x$ are both curves, while the graph of $y = 2x$ is a line. The graph of $y = 2 \div x$ has two separate pieces, while the other graphs have one piece. In the first equation, 2 is multiplied by x, in the second 2 is divided by x, and in the third, 2 is the base and x is the exponent.)

When you feel most students are reaching a comfort level with making calculator graphs, move on to Question A. You may want to read the question together and ask students to explain why the equation given makes sense.

Have students work in small groups on the problem. Try to put a student who is skilled at making calculator graphs in each group.

(**Explore** 4.2)

For Question A, be sure students use the window settings provided. This way they can check with each other to see whether they have made an appropriate graph.

As you walk around, check to see that students understand the mechanics of using a calculator to produce a graph and give assistance where needed.

Remind students that in order to trace, the cursor must be on the graph. Ask students if it is easy for them to find exact values for (x, y) pairs using the $\boxed{\text{TRACE}}$ key.

Ask students why it may be necessary to adjust the calculator window when graphing different equations. If students are having difficulty with the window, suggest they compute some low and high values to find the range.

(**Summarize** 4.2)

Have students share their answers and explain their thinking.

Suggested Questions These questions can help focus students on the important ideas:

- *What do the window settings given for A(2) mean? Relate your answer to the situation in the problem.* (The window will show only the part of the graph where the number of sections is between 0 and 15 and the number of rods is between 0 and 50.)

You may want to make a sketch of the graph on the overhead or board.

- *As you trace the graph, if the coordinates given on the bottom of the screen are about $x = 5.90$ and $y = 18.71$, what does this mean in terms of the problem setting?* (It means that it will take about 18.71 rods to build about 5.9 sections. Since the number of rods and sections must be whole numbers, it means that 6 sections need about 19 rods.)

- *What does the point (7.5, 23.5) mean in this context?* (That it would take 23.5 rods to build 7.5 sections. However, this does not make sense in this situation.)

- *What viewing window did you use for Question B?* (Settings will vary. The settings $Xmin = 0, Xmax = 25, Ymin = 0, Ymax = 100$ give a good view of the graph.)

- *Did anyone try a setting that gave axes but no line? If so, what does that mean?* (It means that the graph lies outside of the viewing area.)

Going Further

- *In Question B, what are the coordinates of the point where the line crosses the y-axis? What does this tell you about the bonus-card situation?* (The coordinates are (0, 100). This means the card has 100 bonus points when no rides have been taken.)

- *Where does the line cross the x-axis? What does this tell you?* (Between $x = 16$ and $x = 17$. The value of y is 0 where the line crosses the x-axis. This means that the bonus-point balance of the card will be near 0 after 16 rides. There is no exact number of rides that gives a balance of 0. After 16 rides, the balance is small, but greater than 0. After 17 rides, the graph shows that the balance is less than 0, which doesn't make sense. Although there are some points left after 16 rides, there are not enough points to use for another ride.)

<table>
<tr><td>4.2</td><td colspan="2"><h1>Making and Using Calculator Graphs</h1></td><td>At a Glance</td></tr>
</table>

PACING $1\frac{1}{2}$ days

Mathematical Goal

• Make and use graphical representations on a graphing calculator

Launch

Before making their first graph, have students erase equations entered in their calculators, turn off any plots, and set the window to the standard settings.

Use the discussion in the student book to introduce making, adjusting, and tracing a calculator graph. Use an overhead graphing calculator, Transparency 4.2A, or the student book to help with the discussion.

Use the Getting Ready to allow students to experiment with graphing on a graphing calculator.

• *Which, if any, of the graphs show similar patterns of change? How are the graphs similar? How are the equations of the graphs similar?*

• *How are the graphs different? How are the equations for the graphs different?*

You may want to read Question A together and ask students to explain why the equation given makes sense.

Have students work in small groups. Try to put a student who is skilled at making calculator graphs in each group.

Materials
• Graphing calculator
• Transparencies 4.2A and 4.2B (optional)
• Overhead graphing calculator (optional)

Explore

As you walk around, check to see that students understand the mechanics of using a calculator to produce a graph and give assistance where needed.

Remind students that in order to trace, the cursor must be on the graph. Ask students if it is easy for them to find exact values for (x, y) pairs using the TRACE key.

Ask students why it may be necessary to adjust the calculator window when graphing different equations.

Materials
• Graphing calculators

Summarize

Have students share their answers and explain their thinking.

• *What do the window settings given for Question A mean? Relate your answer to the situation in the problem.*

• *As you trace the graph, if the coordinates given on the bottom of the screen are about $x = 5.90$ and $y = 18.71$, what does this mean in terms of the problem setting?*

• *What does the point (7.5, 23.5) mean in this context?*

• *What viewing window did you use for Question B?*

• *Did anyone try a setting that gave axes but no line? If so, what does that mean?*

Materials
• Graphing calculators
• Student notebooks
• Transparency 4.2C

continued on next page

continued

Going Further

- *In Question B, what are the coordinates of the point where the line crosses the y–axis? What does this tell you about the bonus-card situation?*

- *Where does the line cross the x-axis? What does this tell you about the situation?*

ACE Assignment Guide for Problem 4.2

Differentiated Instruction
Solutions for All Learners

Core 2, 4, 17
Other *Applications* 3; *Connections* 13–16; unassigned choices from previous problems

Adapted For suggestions about adapting ACE exercises, see the *CMP Special Needs Handbook.*
Connecting to Prior Units 15: *Shapes and Designs;* 16: *Covering and Surrounding*

Answers to Problem 4.2

A. 1. The formula is correct. Possible explanation: For one section, you need a set of three rods plus one rod on the bottom, or $3 + 1$ rods. For two sections, you need two sets of three rods plus one rod on the bottom, or $3 \times 2 + 1$ rods. For three sections, you need three sets of three rods plus one rod on the bottom, or $3 \times 3 + 1$ rods. This pattern continues, so for s sections, you need $3s + 1$ rods.

2. Points are added in part (3).

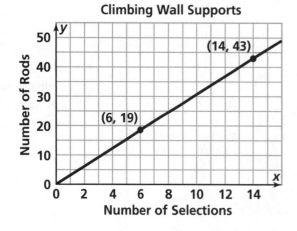

Climbing Wall Supports

3. $(6, 19)$ and $(14, 43)$; See graph in part (2).

4. 6 sections are made up of 19 rods and 14 sections are made up of 43 rods.

5. $n = 9$. The point $(9, 28)$ means that when 28 rods are used, there will be 9 sections.

B. 1. Scales and labels will vary.

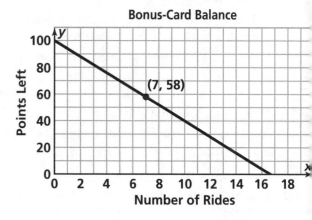

Bonus-Card Balance

2. When 58 points are left, 7 rides have been taken.

3. $(13, 22)$. When 22 points are left, 13 rides have been taken.

Extending the Tour

Goals

- Use a graphing calculator to support problem solving

- Practice equation writing and solving using paper-and-pencil and calculator methods

This problem helps students see how a graphing calculator can support their reasoning in the problem-solving process. It also gives them additional practice with writing an equation for a relationship and solving problems either with pencil and paper or a graphing calculator.

Students must plot bike-rental price information for two companies on the same axes and use the graphs to analyze and compare the information. The two graphs intersect, and students must think about what the values on either side of the intersection point tell them about the situation.

Launch 4.3

Introduce the problem context by looking at the two price quotes with the students.

Suggested Questions Ask questions such as these to engage students in the problem:

- *What question do the tour operators need to answer?* (Which company offers a better deal?)

- *How would you find the price for renting 30 bikes from each of the companies?* (For Cycle the Coast, multiply the number of customers by $25. For Speedy Wheels multiply the number of bikes by $20 and then add $100 for pickup and delivery.)

- *What would be a reasonable approach for figuring out what company to use?* (Possible answer: Make graphs or tables to help you compare the two quotes. Or, write equations and use them to figure out when each company is cheaper.)

- *If you want to use your graphing calculator what do you need to do?* (Write an equation relating the cost to the number of bikes for each company.)

- *Before you write your equation, you will review what you have learned about making a table and a graph by hand. You can use your graphing calculators to check your work. This is where you will need to have an equation for each business.*

When you feel the students are ready, have them work in pairs or small groups on the problem.

Explore 4.3

Remind students to plot the data for both companies on the same axes but to use a different color or symbol for each company. They should make a key to show which company each color or symbol represents.

As you circulate, make note of problems students are having and be sure to address these with questions in the summary. Also look for students who are showing confidence with the process of representing situations in tables, graphs, and equations. Call on these students in the summary to describe the process they used to make sense of the problem.

Some students will want to use the graphing calculator from the beginning. Explain to these students that they should first try to make a table and graph without a calculator. This will help them understand what the numbers mean and how they are calculated. This process is also very helpful in monitoring whether information from the graphing calculator is accurate. Perhaps most importantly, it helps students learn better how to interpret what graphing calculator tables and graphs mean and show.

Summarize 4.3

The summary reviews all that was accomplished in this investigation as well as in earlier investigations. You can ask the kinds of questions that have been asked throughout this unit. Also, you can incorporate the Mathematical Reflections questions into this summary.

Suggested Questions Ask questions such as the following:

- *Which bike-rental company seems best for the tour business? Why?* (It depends on what number of customers are going on a tour. For some numbers Cycle the Coast is better and for others Speedy Wheels is better.)

- *For what number of bikes are the costs for the two companies the same?* (20 bikes)

Note that this is a case of solving a pair of simultaneous linear equations, but students will not formally meet this idea until grade 8. Here the work is all informal sense-making.

- *How does the table show where the costs are the same?* (In the row for 20 bikes, the cost values for the two companies are the same.)

- *How does the graph show where the costs are the same?* (At the intersection point, the number of bikes and rental costs are the same for both companies. The x-coordinate of this point gives you the number of bikes for which the costs are the same, and the y-coordinate tells you what that cost is.)

- *What other useful information is obtained by analyzing both graphs on the same coordinate grid?* (Possible answers: You can see that the graphs cross the y-axis at different points. This tells you the "starting point" for the costs at each company. The graph for Cycle the Coast starts at $(0, 0)$, indicating that the cost for 0 bikes is $0. The graph for Speedy Wheels crosses at $(0, 100)$, indicating that the cost for 0 bikes is $100. This is the fixed pick-up-and-delivery cost. You can read the costs for any number of bikes for either company that interests you.)

- *Who can summarize what you do to make a table on a graphing calculator that shows how two variables are related?*

- *Who can summarize what you do to make a graph on a graphing calculator that shows how two variables are related?*

- *What makes a graph useful?* (It shows in a picture how the dependent variable changes as the independent variable increases. It can also show how two graphs on the same axis are related.)

- *What makes a table useful?* (You can read off specific values for the independent variable that is of interest. You can also search the independent column to find what goes with a particular value of the independent variable.)

4.3 Extending the Tour

Mathematical Goals

- Use a graphing calculator to support problem solving
- Practice equation writing and solving using paper-and-pencil and calculator methods

Launch

Look at the two price quotes with students.

- *What question do the tour operators need to answer?*
- *How would you find the price for renting 30 bikes from each of the companies?*
- *What would be a reasonable approach for figuring out what company to use?*
- *If you want to use your graphing calculator what do you need to do?*

Explain that, before students write equations, they will review what they have learned about making a table and a graph by hand.

Have students work in pairs or small groups.

Materials
- Transparencies 4.3A and 4.3B

Explore

Remind students to plot the data for both companies on the same graph but to use a different color or symbol for each company.

As you circulate, make note of problems students are having and address these in the summary. Look for students who are showing confidence with representing relationships. Call on these students in the summary to explain the problem-solving processes.

Be sure students make a table and graph without the calculator.

Materials
- Graphing calculators
- Grid paper

Summarize

Consider incorporating Mathematical Reflections into the summary.

Ask questions such as the following:

- *Which bike-rental company seems best for the tour business? Why?*
- *For what number of bikes are the costs for the two companies the same?*
- *How does the table show where the costs are the same?*
- *How does the graph show where the costs are the same?*
- *What other useful information is obtained by analyzing both graphs on the same coordinate grid?*
- *Who can summarize what you do to make a table on a graphing calculator that shows how two variables are related?*
- *Who can summarize what you do to make a graph on a graphing calculator that shows how two variables are related?*
- *What makes a graph useful? What makes a table useful?*

Materials
- Student notebooks

ACE Assignment Guide for Problem 4.3

Differentiated Instruction
Solutions for All Learners

Core 5, 6

Other *Extensions* 18, 19; unassigned choices from previous problems

Adapted For suggestions about adapting Exercise 5 and other ACE exercises, see the *CMP Special Needs Handbook.*
Connecting to Prior Units 18: *How Likely Is It?*

Answers to Problem 4.3

A.

Price Quote Comparison

Number of Bikes	Cycle the Coast Cost	Speedy Wheels Cost
5	$125	$200
10	$250	$300
15	$375	$400
20	$500	$500
25	$625	$600
30	$750	$700
35	$875	$800
40	$1,000	$900

B.

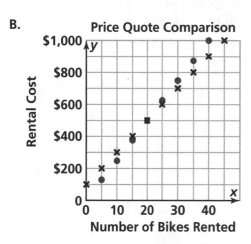

Price Quote Comparison

Cycle the Coast = ●   Speedy Wheels = ✕

C. Cycle the Coast: $c = 25n$;
Speedy Wheels: $c = 100 + 20n$
In both equations, n is the number of bikes rented and c is the cost.

D. They look very much the same.

E. The costs are the same for 20 bikes. You can tell by looking at the row in the table where the costs are the same for both companies. On the graph, the intersection of the two lines tells you when the costs for both companies are equal.

F. The intersection point shows where the costs are the same for both companies. The x-coordinate of the intersection point is the number of bikes for which the cost is the same. To the left of the point of intersection, Cycle the Coast is the better deal. To the right of the point of intersection, Speedy Wheels is the better deal. You need to read off the numbers of bikes that are the x-values on either side.

G. If fewer than 20 people go on the tour, then the tour operators should rent from Cycle the Cost. If more than 20 people go, then they should rent from Speedy Wheels. For exactly 20 people, the costs are the same so it doesn't matter from which company they rent.

The student edition pages for this
investigation begin on the next page.

Notes

Calculator Tables and Graphs

In the last investigation, you wrote equations to describe patterns and to show how variables are related. Such equations are used in mathematics, science, economics, and many other subject areas. Tables, graphs, and equations are all useful ways of representing relationships between variables. When you have an equation relating variables, you can use a *graphing calculator* to make a graph or table of the relationship quickly.

4.1 Making and Using Calculator Tables

Suppose you want to use your calculator to make a table of values for the formulas for the circumference C and area A of a circle with radius r:

$$C = 2\pi r \text{ and } A = \pi r^2.$$

To enter the equations into your calculator, press **Y=** to get a screen like the one below.

```
Plot1 Plot2 Plot3
\Y1 = █
\Y2 =
\Y3 =
\Y4 =
\Y5 =
\Y6 =
\Y7 =
```

64   Variables and Patterns

Notes _____

_____

_____

_____

On most calculators, you enter the independent variable as X; the dependent variable is Y. Enter the equation for circumference as Y1 and the equation for area as Y2 as shown below.

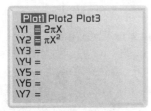

Next, press 2nd TblSet and enter the table settings shown below. The settings indicate that the x-values (radius values) in the table should start at 0 and increase in steps of 1.

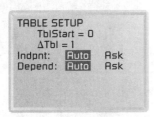

Press 2nd TABLE, and you will see the table.

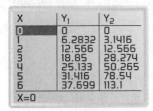

You can use the scroll keys to see more values for radius, circumference, and area.

Getting Ready for Problem

- What does the number 28.274 in the third column mean?
- What does 25.133 in the second column mean?
- What does 5 in the first column mean?

Notes _____

_____

_____

_____

In the following problem, you will use calculator tables to explore relationships between variables. You will scan the tables to solve problems or look for interesting patterns in the entries.

Problem 4.1 Making and Using Calculator Tables

A. The equation $p = 50 + 10n$ represents the Wild World admission price in dollars p for a group of n people. To study this relationship, enter the equation Y1 = 50 + 10X into your calculator.

  1. Make a calculator table showing (n, p) values for $n = 1, 2, 3$, and so on.

  2. Scan the table to find the admission price for a group of 26 people.

  3. Find the value of n for which $p = 480$. Explain what this entry tells you about the admission price and the number of people.

  4. Use the table to find the value of n for which $950 = 50 + 10n$. Explain what this table entry tells you about the admission price and the number of people.

B. The equation $d = 2.5t$ represents the distance a canoe team paddles in meters d in t seconds.

  1. Make a calculator table showing (t, d) values for $t = 4, 8, 12$, and so on.

  2. Use the table to find the distance the team paddles in 40 seconds.

  3. Use the table to find the value of t for which $2.5t = 437.5$. Explain what this entry tells you about the time and distance traveled.

C. The equation $b = 100 - 6r$ gives the number of bonus points b left on a Wild World bonus card after r rides.

  1. Make a calculator table showing (r, b) values for $r = 0, 2, 4$, and so on.

  2. How does the number of bonus points change as the number of rides increases in steps of 2? Why does that pattern occur?

  3. Use your table to find a value of r for which $100 - 6r = 10$. (Adjust the table settings if you need to.) Explain what this entry tells you about the number of rides and the bonus points left on the card.

ACE Homework starts on page 72.

66   Variables and Patterns

Notes _____

_____

_____

_____

4.2 Making and Using Calculator Graphs

Graphing calculators can help you make and study graphs. Just as when you make a graph with pencil and paper, the key step is choosing ranges and scales for the axes.

Suppose you want to graph $y = 1.5x + 2$. Press Y= and enter the equation, just as you do when you make a table. Next, set the boundaries of the graphing window. Press WINDOW to see the screen below. The settings shown here are the *standard* window settings.

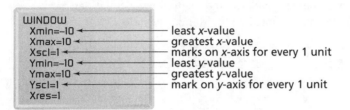

WINDOW
- Xmin=-10 ◄——————— least *x*-value
- Xmax=10 ◄——————— greatest *x*-value
- Xscl=1 ◄——————— marks on *x*-axis for every 1 unit
- Ymin=-10 ◄——————— least *y*-value
- Ymax=10 ◄——————— greatest *y*-value
- Yscl=1 ◄——————— mark on *y*-axis for every 1 unit
- Xres=1

Press GRAPH to see what the graph looks like in this window.

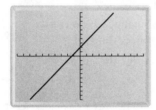

Suppose you want to focus on the part of the graph that shows positive *x*- and *y*-values. Press WINDOW again and change the settings. Use the settings shown below at the left. Then press GRAPH to see the screen on the right.

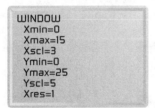

WINDOW
- Xmin=0
- Xmax=15
- Xscl=3
- Ymin=0
- Ymax=25
- Yscl=5
- Xres=1

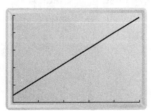

Investigation 4 Calculator Tables and Graphs **67**

Notes _____

_____

_____

_____

To find coordinates of particular points on the graph, press [TRACE]. Use the arrow keys to move the cursor along the graph and see coordinates of highlighted points.

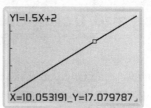

When the cusor is on the line, the coordinates appear at the bottom of the screen and the equation appears in the upper left.

Getting Ready for Problem 4.2

Experiment with your graphing calculator and the following equations. Graph one set of equations at a time. Use the standard window.

Set 1	Set 2	Set 3	Set 4
$y = 3x - 4$	$y = 5$	$y = 2x + 3$	$y = 2x$
$y = x^2$	$y = 3x$	$y = 2x - 5$	$y = 2 \div x$
$y = 3x + 2$	$y = 1x$	$y = (0.5)x + 2$	$y = 2^x$

Answer the following questions for each set of equations.

- Which, if any, of the graphs show similar patterns of change? How are the graphs similar? How are the equations for the graphs similar?
- How are the graphs different? How are the equations for the graphs different?

Problem 4.2 Making and Using Calculator Graphs

A. One popular attraction at Wild World is the climbing wall. Supports for the wall are frames of squares made from steel rods. The number of rods depends on the number of square sections in the frame.

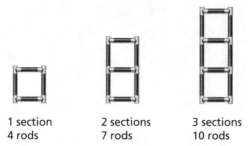

1 section
4 rods

2 sections
7 rods

3 sections
10 rods

68 Variables and Patterns

Notes _____

_____

_____

_____

1. An engineer at Wild World wrote the equation $r = 3s + 1$ to relate the number of sections and the number of rods. Do you think this formula is correct? Explain. What does each variable in the equation represent?

2. Use your calculator to graph the engineer's equation. Use the window settings Xmin = 0, Xmax = 15, Ymin = 0, and Ymax = 50. Sketch your graph on axes like these. Give your graph a title.

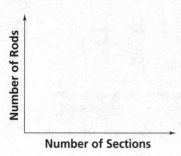

3. Press TRACE and use the arrow keys to move along the graph. Locate a point with a *y*-value of about 19. Mark this point on your sketch and label it with its coordinates. Then, find a point with a *y*-value of about 43. Mark and label this point on your sketch.

4. Explain what the coordinates of each point in part (3) tell you about the number of sections and the number of rods.

5. Use your calculator graph to find a value of *s* for which $3s + 1 = 28$. Give the coordinates of that point, and explain what they tell you about sections and rods.

B. Make a calculator graph of $b = 100 - 6r$, which gives the bonus card balance *b* after *r* rides. Experiment with the window settings until you have a good view of the graph. (You might find it helpful to look at the table you made in Problem 4.1.)

1. Make a sketch of the graph. Label the axes with variable names and scales. Add a descriptive title to your graph.

2. Find a point on the calculator graph for which $b \approx 58$. (The symbol $\approx$ means "is approximately equal to.") Mark this point on your sketch and label it with its coordinates. Explain what the coordinates tell you about the number of rides taken and the balance on the card.

3. Use your calculator graph to find a value of *r* for which $100 - 6r \approx 22$. Give the coordinates of that point and explain what they tell you about the rides taken and the card balance.

ACE Homework starts on page 72.

Notes _____

_____

_____

_____

4.3 Extending the Tour

The bike tour was a success! So many people signed up for the tour that the students decide to offer an additional two-day bike tour. Two bike rental companies submit bids to the students. Their price quotes are shown here.

123 Surf Street
555-bike

CYCLE THE COAST
Bike Sales and Rentals

Price Quote for   Ocean Bike Tours

Bikes delivered and picked up
each day for two days.

Price: $25 per bike for two days

SPEEDY WHEELS
Bikes and Skateboards
72 Market Street
555-spin

Speedy Wheels

PRICE QUOTE

Customer: _____ Ocean Bike Tours
Item: _____ Touring bikes, various sizes
Time: _____ 2 days
Price: _____ $100 for pickup and delivery,
plus $20 per bike for two days

In the next problem, you will use your graphing calculator to analyze the price quotes and advise Ocean Bike Tours about which company to use.

Notes _____

_____

_____

_____

Study the price quotes from the two companies. The following questions
will help you analyze the information.

A. Make a table showing the costs for renting bikes from each company.
Include costs for 5, 10, 15, 20, 25, 30, 35, and 40 bikes in your table.

B. Plot the (*number of bikes, rental cost*) data for both companies on a
graph like the one below. Use a different color or plotting symbol for
each company.

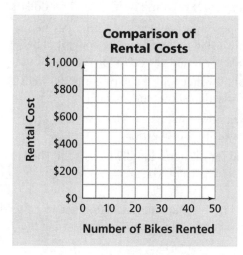

C. For each company, write an equation relating the number of bikes
rented to the total cost. Tell what the letter variables in your equation
represent.

D. Enter your equations into your calculator as Y1 and Y2. Graph both
equations in the same window. Compare the calculator graph with the
graph you made by hand.

E. Is there a number of bikes for which both companies charge the same
rental fee? How can the graph help you find the answer?

F. How does the graph show the number of bikes for which Cycle the
Coast is the most economical? How does it show the number of
bikes for which Speedy Wheels offers the better deal?

G. What advice would you give Ocean Bike Tours about which company
to rent bikes from? Use your analysis of the two plans to justify your
advice.

ACE Homework starts on page 72.

Applications

1. Sean bought a DVD player and a receiver. The store offered him an interest-free payment plan with weekly installments. Sean figured out that after *n* weeks of payments, he would still owe $175 - 7.5n$ dollars.

   a. Make a calculator table showing what Sean owes after payments 1, 2, 3, and so on. Study the table to figure out the amount of his weekly payment. How is this amount shown in the table pattern?

   b. Scan the table to find out how much Sean will owe after 20 weeks. Record the (x, y) table entry that shows the answer.

   c. When will the amount Sean owes fall below $100? Which (x, y) table entry shows the answer to this question?

   d. When will Sean have paid for his items in full? How is this shown in the table?

2. Trevor entered an equation into his graphing calculator, and the calculator displayed this graph and table. The graph is shown in the standard window.

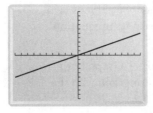 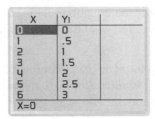

   a. What is the value of *y* when $x = 6$? How is this shown in the table? How is it shown in the graph?

   b. What equation did Trevor enter into his calculator?

3. Ziamara used her calculator to make a graph of $y = 3x$. She noticed that the point $(0, 0)$ was on the graph. Name three other points on the graph. Explain how you found these points.

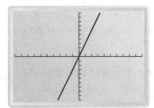

72 Variables and Patterns

Notes _____

4. The operators of Ocean Bike Tours consider leasing a small bus. They compare two companies. Superior Buses charges $5 for each mile driven. East Coast Transport charges $1,000, plus $2.50 per mile driven.

   a. For each company, write an equation to show how the lease cost c depends on number of miles driven m.

   b. Enter both equations into your calculator. Choose window settings that make sense for this situation and that show a good view of both graphs. Sketch the graphs, and tell what axes limits (Xmin, Xmax, Ymin, Ymax) you used.

   c. Press TRACE. Trace your graph to estimate the coordinates of the point at which the lease cost is the same for both companies. Explain what the coordinates of the point tell you about the bus-rental situation.

   d. For what driving mileage would the East Coast lease be a better deal? For what mileage would the Superior Buses lease be better? Explain how your answers are shown on the graph from part (b).

5. The Mudville Manatees won the league baseball championship. The manager of the souvenir shop wants to order special shirts and caps to sell to fans. She does market research and predicts these relationships between price in dollars p and number sold n:

      Shirts: $n = 5{,}000 - 150p$

      Caps: $n = 3{,}000 - 100p$

Use these equations to answer the questions below. Making calculator tables and graphs might help.

   a. What are the projected shirt sales if the price is $20 per shirt?

   b. Suppose the manager wants to sell 3,500 shirts. How much should she charge for each shirt?

   c. What are the projected cap sales if the price is $17 per cap?

   d. Suppose the manager wants to sell 1,800 caps. How much should she charge for each cap?

Notes _____

_____

_____

_____

6. The principal of Lincoln Middle School wants to send her top science students on a field trip to the state science center. The trip costs $250 for a bus and driver, plus $17.50 per student for food and admission.

   a. What equation relates the trip cost c to the number of students who go on the trip n?

   b. What is the cost of sending 30 students? What is the cost for 60 students?

   c. How many students can go if the budget allows a maximum cost of $1,000?

Connections

For Exercises 7–10, use the pattern to find the missing entries. Then, write an equation relating the two variables.

7.

a	0	1	2	3	■	8	20	100
b	0	7	14	21	28	■	■	■

8.

x	0	1	2	3	4	8	20	100
y	6	7	8	9	■	■	■	■

9.

m	0	1	2	3	4	8	20	100
n	1	3	5	7	■	■	■	■

10.

r	0	1	2	3	4	6	10	20
s	0	1	4	9	16	■	■	■

11. José used his graphing calculator to find the whole-number factors of 960. Here are the steps he followed:

   Step 1: Enter the equation $y = 960 \div x$.
   Step 2: Set TblStart $= 1$ and $_\Delta$Tbl $= 1$.
   Step 3: Scan the table, looking for whole numbers in the y column.

   a. Use José's strategy. Make a list of the factor pairs for 960.

   b. Explain why José's strategy works for 960. How could you modify his strategy to find factors of a different whole number?

   c. What is the greatest x-value you need to check to guarantee you have found all the factors of 960? Explain.

Notes _____

_____

_____

_____

12. Most states add sales tax to the cost of non-food items. Let p stand for the list price of an item, t for the additional amount you must pay due to the sales tax, and c for the total cost of buying the item.

Homework Help Online
PHSchool.com
For: Help with Exercise 12
Web Code: ane-1412

  a. What equation relates c, p, and t?

  b. Suppose a state has a sales tax of 8%. What equation relates t and p? What equation relates c and p?

  c. Enter the equations from part (b) in your calculator. Make a calculator table showing list price, tax, and total cost for items priced from $0 to $100 in steps of $5.

  d. What is the total cost of a non-food item that is priced $65?

13. You have seen that many of the costs for the Ocean Bike Tour depend on the number of customers. This table shows a new relationship between the number of customers and the cost of a ferry ride.

Costs for Ferry Ride

Customers	1	2	3	4	5	6	7	8	9
Ferry Cost	$2.50	$5.00	$7.50	$10.00	$12.50	$15.00	$17.50	$20.00	$22.50

  a. Write an equation for the rule relating ferry cost f and number of customers n.

  b. Use your equation to find the cost if 35 people are on the tour.

  c. How many people can go on the ferry if the tour leader has $75?

14. Look back at Exercise 12 in Investigation 1. The first graph shown is the relationship between Amanda's hunger and the time of day. Could you represent this relationship in a table? Could you represent this relationship with an equation? Explain.

'otes _____

_____

_____

_____

15. You know from your work with polygons that one way to find the sum of the interior angles of a polygon is to divide the shape into triangles by drawing diagonals from one of the vertices, as shown below.

3 sides
0 diagonals

4 sides
1 diagonal

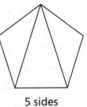
5 sides
2 diagonals

a. Copy and complete the table below. The last row should contain formulas for *D*, *S*, and *A* for a regular polygon with *n* sides. (Remember that a *regular polygon* is a polygon in which all sides are the same length and all angles are the same size.)

Regular Polygons

Number of Sides, *n*	Number of Diagonals, *D* (from a single vertex)	Sum of Interior Angles, *S*	Size of Each Angle if Polygon is Regular, *A*
3	0	180°	60°
4	■	■	■
5	■	■	■
6	■	■	■
⋮	⋮	⋮	⋮
n	*D* = ■	*S* = ■	*A* = ■

b. Enter your formula for *D* into your calculator. Use a table or graph to find the number of sides a polygon must have if you can draw exactly 10 diagonals from a single vertex.

c. Enter your formula for *S* into your calculator. Use a table or graph to find the sum of the angles for a polygon with 10 sides.

d. Enter your formula for *A* into your calculator. Using a table or graph, look at the *A* values for polygons with up to 20 sides. Identify (by giving the number of sides) all regular polygons that have whole number interior angle measures.

Notes _____

_____

_____

_____

16. The area, A, of a circle is related to the radius, r, by the equation $A = \pi r^2$. Enter this formula into your calculator. Use a calculator graph or table to estimate the answers to the questions below. Make your estimates correct to the nearest tenth.

   a. What is the radius of a circle that has area 144 square inches (1 square foot)?

   b. What is the radius of a circle that has area 9 square feet (1 square yard)?

Extensions

17. In this unit, you have studied a variety of relationships between variables. The equations below are simple cases of three important types of patterns of change.

$$y_1 = 2x \qquad\qquad y_2 = x^2 \qquad\qquad y_3 = \frac{3}{x}$$

   a. For each equation, make a table of (x, y) values for $x = 0, 1, 2, 3$, and so on. Describe the pattern of change in each table by completing this sentence:

   As the value of x *increases, the value of* y _____.

   Be as precise as you can in describing the patterns. Then, compare each individual pattern of change with the others.

   b. Graph the three equations in the same viewing window, with Xmin = 0, Xmax = 5, Ymin = 0, and Ymax = 15. Describe the patterns of change shown by the graphs. Explain how each pattern can be predicted by thinking about the calculations required to find y from x.

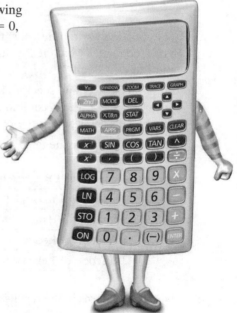

Investigation 4 Calculator Tables and Graphs   **77**

otes _____

_____

_____

_____

18. You can use your graphing calculator to simulate probability experiments that involve rolling dice or flipping coins.

a. Press Y= .

```
Plot1 Plot2 Plot3
\Y1 = ▪
\Y2 =
\Y3 =
\Y4 =
\Y5 =
\Y6 =
\Y7 =
```

Then, press MATH , highlight PRB on the top of the screen, and press 5 to select "randInt(."

```
MATH  NUM  CPX  PRB
1 :rand
2 :nPr
3 :nCr
4 :!
5 :randInt(
6 :randNorm(
7 :randBin(
```

You will be back to the Y= screen. Complete the equation by typing 0) 1) .

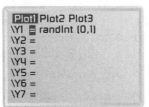

The equation $y = \text{randInt}(0, 1)$ randomly gives a y-value of either 0 or 1, no matter what the x-value is. Consider 0 to mean "heads" and 1 to mean "tails."

Press 2nd TblSet and specify TblStart = 1 and ΔTb = 1. Then press 2nd TABLE . The X column counts the coin tosses, and the Y1 column tells you whether the result is heads (0) or tails (1).

Copy and complete the table below.

Graphing Calculator Coin Tossing

Number of Tosses	5	10	20	30	40	50
Number of Heads	▪	▪	▪	▪	▪	▪
Fraction of Heads	▪	▪	▪	▪	▪	▪
Fraction of Tails	▪	▪	▪	▪	▪	▪

Describe patterns in the results. Are the results what you would expect? Explain.

Notes _____

_____

_____

_____

b. Revise the procedures of part (a) to simulate rolling a fair die 50 times. Calculate the number of times and fraction of times the outcome 1 occurs in the 50 rolls. Are the results what you would expect? Explain. (**Hint:** The equation $y = \text{randInt}(3, 5)$ randomly gives a y-value of 3, 4, or 5. The equation $y = \text{randInt}(13, 17)$ randomly gives a y-value of 13, 14, 15, 16, or 17. What equation would give random dice rolls?)

19. The bike tour holds a 30-mile race on the last day. They give the two youngest riders, Tony and Sarah, a half-hour head start. For this first half hour, Tony and Sarah ride at a steady pace of 12 miles per hour. Then, they keep up a steady pace of about 10 miles per hour. When the others start riding, they go at a steady pace of about 15 miles per hour.

a. Write an equation for the distance d in miles Tony and Sarah travel in t hours.

b. Write an equation for the distance d in miles the other riders travel in t hours.

c. Use the equations from parts (a) and (b) to make a table and a graph showing the relationship between distance and time for the two groups of riders.

d. Will the older riders catch up with Tony and Sarah before the end of the 30-mile race? Explain using both the table and the graph.

otes

Mathematical Reflections 4

In this investigation, you used a graphing calculator to help you understand relationships between variables. These questions will help you summarize what you have learned.

Think about your answers to these questions. Discuss your ideas with other students and your teacher. Then write a summary of your findings in your notebook.

1. **a.** Describe the steps required to make a calculator table that shows how two variables are related.

   b. How can you scan a calculator table to answer questions about a relationship?

2. **a.** Describe the steps required to make a calculator graph that shows how two variables are related.

   b. How can you trace a calculator graph to answer questions about a relationship?

3. What are the advantages and disadvantages of using tables and graphs to solve problems and search for patterns? In what ways is using a calculator more useful than using paper-and-pencil methods? In what ways is it less useful?

Notes _____

_____

_____

_____

Investigation 4

ACE
Assignment Choices

Differentiated
Instruction
Solutions for All Learners

Problem 4.1

Core 1
Other *Connections* 7–12

Problem 4.2

Core 2, 4, 17
Other *Applications* 3; *Connections* 13–16;
unassigned choices from previous problems

Problem 4.3

Core 5, 6, 19
Other *Extensions* 18; unassigned choices from
previous problems

Adapted For suggestions about adapting
Exercise 5 and other ACE exercises, see the
CMP *Special Needs Handbook*

Connecting to Prior Units 11: *Prime Time;* 12: *Bits
and Pieces III;* 15: *Shapes and Designs;* 16:
Covering and Surrounding; 18: *How Likely Is It?*

Applications

1. a.

X	Y₁
1	167.5
2	160
3	152.5
4	145
5	137.5
6	130
7	122.5
X=1	

Sean's weekly payment is $7.50, because on
the table his debt decreases each week by
$7.50.

b. After 20 weeks, Sean will owe $25. This is
shown by the table entry (20, 25).

c. After 10 weeks, Sean will owe exactly $100.
After 11 weeks, he will owe less than $100.
This is shown by the entries (10, 100) and
(11, 92.5).

d. Sean will have paid for his items in full on
week 24. The table gives a balance of $2.50
after week 23 and of –$5 after week 24. So,
Sean will make his last payment, which was
only $2.50 on week 24.

2. a. When $x = 6$, $y = 3$. This is shown on the
graph by the point (6, 3).

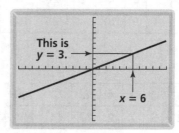

b. $y = \frac{1}{2}x$

3. Possible answer: (1, 3), (2, 6), (3, 9). Students
can determine these values from the graph or
equation.

4. a. Superior: $c = 5m$
East Coast: $c = 1,000 + 2.5m$;

b. Axes limits will vary. One possibility is
Xmin = 0, Xmax = 1,000, Xscl = 100,
Ymin = 0, Ymax = 5,000, Yscl = 500

c. (400, 2,000); For a distance of 400 miles, the
rental costs for both companies will be
$2,000.

d. East Coast is a better deal when mileage is
over 400 miles. On the graph, the line for
East Coast is beneath the graph for
Superior for x-values greater than 400.
Superior is a better deal when mileage is
less than 400 miles. On the graph, the line
for Superior is beneath the graph for East
Coast for x-values less than 400.

5. a. 2,000 shirts   **b.** $10

   c. 1,300 caps   **d.** $12

6. a. $c = 250 + 17.50n$

   b. It will cost \$775 to send 30 students and \$1,300 to send 60 students.

   c. 42 students

Connections

7.

a	0	1	2	3	4	8	20	100
b	0	7	14	21	28	56	140	700

$b = 7a$

8.

x	0	1	2	3	4	8	20	100
y	6	7	8	9	10	14	26	106

$y = x + 6$

9.

m	0	1	2	3	4	8	20	100
n	1	3	5	7	9	17	41	201

$n = 2m + 1$

10.

r	0	1	2	3	4	6	10	20
s	0	1	4	9	16	36	100	400

$s = r \times r$ or $s = r^2$

11. a. 1 and 960, 2 and 480, 3 and 320, 4 and 240, 5 and 192, 6 and 160, 8 and 120, 10 and 96, 12 and 80, 15 and 64, 16 and 60, 20 and 48, 24 and 40, 30 and 32

   b. The strategy divides 960 by every possible whole number in order, starting with 1. These values are represented by the x-values in the table. The y-column shows the result of the division. When the result is a whole number, it means the x-value is a factor of 960. The corresponding y-value is the other number in the factor pair. To modify the strategy for a different whole number, just change the 960 in the equation to that whole number.

   c. The largest value that needs to be checked is the whole number closest to the square root of 960. Once you try all factors less than that number, the other factors will have already been used in another factor pair.

12. a. $c = t + p$

   b. $t = 0.08p$; $c = 0.08p + p$

   c.

X	Y1	Y2
0	0	0
5	.4	5.4
10	.8	10.8
15	1.2	16.2
20	1.6	21.6
25	2	27
30	2.4	32.4
X=0		

   d. \$70.20; $c = 0.08(\$65) + \$65 = \$70.20$

13. a. $f = 2.50n$

   b. \$87.50; since $f = 2.50 \times 35$, $f = 87.50$

   c. 30 people; $75 = 2.50n$, so $n = \frac{75}{2.5}$, so $n = 30$

14. Yes, these data could be represented in a table because there are corresponding x- and y-values; however, low, medium, and high levels of hunger would need to be quantified. It could not be stated with a rule because there is not a consistent relationship.

15. a. (Figure 1)

    b. 13 sides

    c. 1440°

    d. 3, 4, 5, 6, 8, 9, 10, 12, 15, 18, and 20

16. a. Approximately 6.77 inches

    b. Approximately 1.7 feet

Extensions

17. a. The table should begin like this:

x	$y_1 = 2x$	$y_2 = x^2$	$y_3 = \frac{3}{x}$
0	0	0	Undefined
1	2	1	3
2	4	4	1.5
3	6	9	1
4	8	16	0.75
5	10	25	0.6
6	12	36	0.5

For $y = 2x$, as the value of x increases, the value of y increases. Specifically, each time x increases by 1, y increases by 2.
For $y = x^2$, as the value of x increases, the value of y increases. Specifically, as x increases in intervals of 1, y increases by 1, then 3, then 5, then 7, and so on. So, y is increasing at a faster and faster rate.
For $y = \frac{3}{x}$, as the value of x increases by 1, the value of y decreases, rapidly at first and then more slowly, approaching 0 as a limit.

    b. The graph of the first equation is a straight line because there is a constant change of 2. The second graph increases slowly at first and then increases faster and faster. This make sense because, when you square the numbers, they get large quickly, faster than if you just multiply them by a fixed number. The third graph goes down and to the right and approaches 0 as x increases. This makes sense because you are dividing 3 by progressively greater numbers.

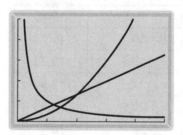

Figure 1

Number of Sides, n	Number of Diagonals, D (from a single vertex)	Sum of Interior Angles, S	Size of each Angle if Polygon is Regular, A
3	0	180°	60°
4	1	360°	90°
5	2	540°	108°
6	3	720°	120°
⋮	⋮	⋮	⋮
n	$D = n - 3$	$S = (n - 2) \times 180$	$A = \frac{(n - 2) \times 180}{n}$

18. a. Answers will vary because the calculator will select different values for each student. However, the fraction of heads should get closer and closer to 0.5 as the number of trials increases. The fraction of tails is always 1 – *fraction of heads*.

  b. To simulate rolling a fair die, you use Y_1=randInt(1,6). The fraction of 1s rolled should approach $\frac{1}{6}$, or 0.167, as the number of trials increases. However, it may take a while for this value to get close to $\frac{1}{6}$.

19. a. $d = 6 + 10t$

  b. $d = 15t$

  c. Tables will vary. Sample:

Time (hr)	Distance for Tony & Sarah	Distance for Others
0	6	0
0.25	8.5	3.75
0.5	11	7.5
0.75	13.5	11.25
1	16	15
1.25	18.5	18.75
1.5	21	22.5
1.75	23.5	26.25
2	26	30

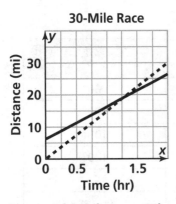

30-Mile Race

Tony and Sarah —— Others - - -

  d. Yes, this can be noticed on the table after about 1.25 hours when the other riders have traveled farther than Tony and Sarah. On the graph, this is where the two lines cross. At this point, the other riders meet Tony and Sarah.

Possible Answers to Mathematical Reflections

1. a. First, press $\boxed{Y=}$ and enter the equation. Then adjust the start value and the table change value, as appropriate. Then display the table.

  b. Use the arrow keys to scan the table.

2. a. First, press $\boxed{Y=}$ and enter the equation. Then, adjust the minimum and maximum values for the x- and y-axes and the scales for each axis, as appropriate. Then display the graph.

  b. Press $\boxed{TRACE}$ to scan the graph. Use the arrow keys to move along the graph. The x- and y-values for your position on the graph will be displayed on the bottom of the screen.

3. An equation can be developed more easily from a table. The rate of change can be observed and more easily compared to others from the graph. Calculators can be much more useful for graphing than paper and pencil methods because they save time and allow you to manipulate the graphs more quickly in order to analyze relationships. Tables and graphs give approximate values for some situations.

For the Teachers In general, graphs and tables give a kind of insight into relationships between variables that is not always evident from algebraic formulas (until one has studie them pretty thoroughly).

The most powerful value of calculator methods is the fact that regardless of the function rule being studied, the calculator table-scan and graph-trace procedures are th same. With algebraic methods, each type of function has some particular procedural rules that must be learned.

Answers to Looking Back and Looking Ahead

For the Teachers The purpose of this section is to help students review and articulate the key ideas of the unit—first through work on problems that require use of the major concepts and skills and then through responses to broader questions about the underlying mathematical principles and techniques.

In this unit, students learned to identify variables in a variety of situations. They developed understanding and skill required to represent relationships in tables and coordinate graphs, to look for patterns relating independent and dependent variables, and to express those patterns with words and equations. Most important of all, they began developing skills for using tables, graphs, and equations to answer questions about variables.

This is the first unit in the *Connected Mathematics* algebra strand. It lays the foundation for students to develop a solid understanding of the key algebraic ideas. This understanding will continue to grow over the years ahead. In future units, students will apply key ideas to a variety of specific kinds of algebraic relationships and equations.

The questions in this section are designed to have students look back at the Mathematical Highlights at the start of the unit to see what they've learned about algebra thus far. Since this is just the first algebra unit, ideas may not be fully or confidently formed at this point. However, it should be useful for you and your students to reflect on how things have developed thus far. We provide fuller answers than you will get from your students, but hope they will be useful to you as the teacher.

1. **a.** (Figure 2)

   b. Possible answer: Each time the distance increases by 100 miles, the shipping cost increases by $1.

   c. (Figure 3)

   d. $c = 0.01d + 5$

   e. If students are correct, they should get a table and a graph that confirm those that they made by hand.

   f. $9.50

   g. 3,000 miles

2. A quantity that changes or varies

   For the Teachers In traditional treatments of algebra the word "variable" is often defined as "a letter that stands for an unknown number." *Connected Mathematics* students will come to use letters in that way when they focus more specifically on solving equations and manipulating symbolic expressions. However, the concept of variable used in most mathematical applications is much closer to "a measurement or count of some quantity that changes either as time passes or in response to changes in other related quantities."

Figure 2

Distance in Miles	100	200	300	400	500	1,000	1,500	2,000
Shipping Cost	$6	$7	$8	$9	$10	$15	$20	$25

Figure 3

Two-Day Shipping Costs

3. In a relationship between two variables, the dependent variable is the variable whose values depend on values of the other variable, which is called the independent variable. For example, the price for filling up a gas tank depends on the number of gallons needed. The number of gallons is the independent variable and the price is the dependent variable.

For the Teacher When two or more variables are related, it is customary to ask which of the variables is more naturally manipulated or changed intentionally and which is more likely to change in response to changes in other variables. The variables that can be changed intentionally are generally considered the independent variables; the responding variables are generally considered to be the dependent variables.

By long-standing mathematical convention, when the relation being studied involves change over time, time is considered the independent variable. However, there are certainly situations in which time is the dependent variable in a relationship. For instance, as the speed of a car or plane increases, the time of a trip decreases in response. There are also situations in which neither of the variables involved in a relationship can be naturally thought of as the independent or dependent variable—for example, the relationship between length and width for rectangles with fixed perimeter or area. In these cases we simply say that the variables are correlated.

4. Sometimes the y-values change at a constant rate as the x-values increase by a fixed amount. The graphs of such relationships are straight lines. If y increases as x increases, the line slants up from left to right. If y decreases as x increases, the line slants down from left to right. Sometimes y-values change at a faster and faster rate as the x-values increase, and sometimes they change at a slower and slower rate. Graphs of these types of relationships are curves.

For the Teacher Students have encountered a variety of patterns in the tables and graphs of related variables. Many have been linear increasing or decreasing patterns. Some have curved patterns like parabolas or hyperbolas or exponential curves. Some have even more

complex patterns. At this point we hope that students are beginning to develop an ability to interpret graph shapes in terms of patterns of change. The details of relating particular graph shapes to particular function types and symbolic expressions will develop over the next several years.

5. To make a table, you need a relationship between variables (expressed symbolically or verbally if possible), a starting point for the independent variable, and a step size of increases in that variable.

Scanning entries of a table helps you answer questions about specific values that meet problem conditions.

6. To make a graph, you need a relationship between variables. This can be given as an equation, a verbal description, or a table of values. Then, you need to identify the variable that should be on each axis and choose the scales for the axes (based on ranges of the variables). Then, you plot specific points for the relationships. If the values between point make sense, you can connect the points. Graphs tend to give a visual image of the overall pattern of change in a relationship that is easier to grasp than the details of a table. However, graphs are less useful when specific numerical results are needed.

7. To write an equation, it helps to work out several specific numerical examples. Then, look for patterns and relationships among the examples, state the relationship in words, identify the variables involved in the relationship, write the pattern(s) using words to name the variables and symbols for $+$, $-$, $\times$, and $\div$, choose letters to represent the variables, and write an equation showing the relation between the dependent variable and the independent variable.

Once you have an equation and a value for the independent variable, you can calculate a related value for the dependent variable and vice versa. The form of the equation can also be used to identify the family of relationship to which the specific equation belongs. For example, by examining the equation you can learn to determine whether the equation represents a linear relationship and whether the graph crosses the y-axis at the origin or some other point. You can also use the equation to explore the relationship on a graphing calculator.

Equations are abstract, but very efficient, ways to summarize a relationship between two or more variables. Equations for relationships are generally directions for calculating the values of one variable when given values of another.

8. If you represent a relationship between variables with an equation, you can enter it in a calculator and get a table and a graph. Scanning tables and tracing graphs can reveal specific information about the related variables.

Looking Back and Looking Ahead

In this unit, you studied some basic ideas of algebra. You learned ways to use those ideas to solve problems about variables and the patterns relating variables. In particular, you studied how to

Go Online
PHSchool.com

For: Vocabulary Review
Puzzle
Web Code: anj-1051

- recognize situations in which changes in variables are related in useful patterns
- describe patterns of change shown in tables and graphs of data
- construct tables and graphs to display relationships between variables
- use algebraic symbols to write equations relating variables
- use tables, graphs, and equations to solve problems
- use a graphing calculator to construct tables and graphs of relationships and to solve equations

Use Your Understanding: Algebraic Reasoning

To test your understanding of algebraic ideas and your skill in using algebraic techniques, consider how algebra is involved in a business we all depend on—the shipping of packages from town to town, across the country, and around the world.

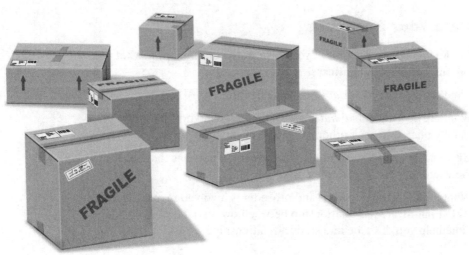

Looking Back and Looking Ahead   **81**

Notes _____

_____

_____

_____

1. A shipping company offers two-day shipping of any package weighing up to 2 pounds for $5 plus $0.01 per mile.

   a. Copy and complete the table.

   Two-Day Shipping Costs

Distance (mi)	100	200	300	400	500	1,000	1,500	2,000
Shipping Cost	■	■	■	■	■	■	■	■

   b. Describe the pattern by which the shipping cost increases as the shipping distance increases.

   c. Make a graph showing shipping charges for distances from 0 to 2,000 miles. Use appropriate labels and scales on the axes.

   d. Write an equation for the relationship between distance d in miles and shipping cost c in dollars.

   e. Use a graphing calculator and the equation in part (d) to check the graph you made in part (c).

   f. Use the table, graph, or equation to find the cost to ship a 1-pound package 450 miles.

   g. Use the table, graph, or equation to figure out how far you can ship a 2-pound package for $35.

Explain Your Reasoning

Answer the following questions in your own words to summarize what you know about variables and patterns.

2. What does the word *variable* mean in algebra?

3. What are *dependent* and *independent variables* and how are they usually related to each other in a problem situation?

4. Give examples that show at least two common patterns that occur in the values of related variables.

5. What are the main decisions and procedures involved in making a table to illustrate the relationship between two variables? How does a table help you describe and study a relationship?

Notes _____

_____

_____

_____

6. What are the main decisions and procedures involved in making a graph to illustrate the relationship between two variables? How does a graph help you describe and study a relationship?

7. What are the main decisions and procedures involved in writing an equation to illustrate the relationship between two variables? How does an equation help you describe and study a relationship?

8. How can you use a graphing calculator to study relationships between variables? What do you need to know about a situation in order to use a calculator? How can the calculator be used to solve problems about variables and relationships?

Look Ahead

Your understanding of algebraic ideas and skills will grow as you work on future *Connected Mathematics* units. You will use variables and symbolic expressions in the geometry unit *Stretching and Shrinking*, the proportional-reasoning unit *Comparing and Scaling*, the algebra unit *Moving Straight Ahead*, and all units in the next *Connected Mathematics* course.

Looking Back and Looking Ahead   **83**

Notes _____

_____

_____

_____

C

change To become different. For example, temperatures rise and fall, prices increase and decrease, and so on. In mathematics, quantities that change are called *variables*.

cambiar Variar, volverse diferente. Por ejemplo, las temperaturas suben y bajan, los precios aumentan y se reducen, y así sucesivamente. En matemática, las cantidades que cambian se llaman *variables*.

coordinate graph A graphical representation of pairs of related numerical values that shows the relationship between two variables. It relates the independent variable (shown on the *x*-axis) and the dependent variable (shown on the *y*-axis).

gráfica de coordenadas Una representación gráfica de pares de valores numéricos asociados que muestra la relación existente entre dos variables. Dicha representación relaciona la variable independiente (mostrada en el eje de las *x*) y la variable dependiente (mostrada en el eje de las *y*).

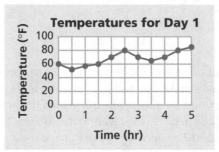

coordinate pair An ordered pair of numbers used to locate a point on a coordinate grid. The first number in a coordinate pair is the value for the *x*-coordinate, and the second number is the value for the *y*-coordinate. A coordinate pair for the graph shown above is (0, 60).

par de coordenadas Un par ordenado de números utilizado para localizar un punto en una cuadrícula de coordenadas. El primer número del par de coordenadas es el valor de la coordenada *x* y el segundo número es el valor de la coordenada *y*. Un par de coordenades para la gráfica que aparece arriba es (0, 60).

D

dependent variable One of the two variables in a relationship. Its value depends upon or is determined by the other variable called the *independent variable*. For example, the cost of a long-distance phone call (dependent variable) depends on how long you talk (independent variable).

variable dependiente Una de las dos variables en una relación. Su valor depende del valor de la otra variable llamada variable independiente, o está determinado por dicho valor. Por ejemplo, el costo de una llamada telefónica de larga distancia (variable dependiente) depende de la duración de la conversación (variable independiente).

E

equation, formula A rule containing variables that represents a mathematical relationship. An example is the formula for finding the area of a circle: $A = \pi r^2$.

ecuación, fórmula Una regla que contiene variables que representa una relación matemática. Un ejemplo de ello es la fórmula para hallar el área de un círculo: $A = \pi r^2$.

84 Variables and Patterns

Notes

independent variable One of the two variables in a relationship. Its value determines the value of the other variable called the *dependent variable*. If you organize a bike tour, for example, the number of people who register to go (independent variable) determines the cost for renting bikes (dependent variable).

variable independiente Una de las dos variables relacionadas. Su valor determina el de la otra variable, llamada variable dependiente. Por ejemplo, si organizas un recorrido en bicicleta, el número de personas inscritas (variable independiente) determina el costo del alquiler de las bicicletas (variable dependiente).

pattern A change that occurs in a predictable way. For example, the squares on a checkerboard form a pattern in which the colors of the squares alternate between red and black. The sequence of square numbers: 1, 4, 9, 16, … forms a pattern in which the numbers increase by the next odd number. That is, 4 is 3 more than 1, 9 is 5 more than 4, 16 is 7 more than 9, and so on.

patrón Una variación que ocurre de manera predecible. Por ejemplo, los cuadrados del tablero de damas forman un patrón en el que los colores de los cuadrados se alternan. La secuencia de números cuadrados: 1, 4, 9, 16, … forma un patrón en el que los números aumentan según la cifra del siguiente número impar. Es decir, 4 es 3 más que 1, 9 es 5 más que 4, 16 es 7 más que 9, y así sucesivamente.

relationship An association between two or more variables. If one of the variables changes, the other variable may also change, and the change may be predictable.

relación Una asociación entre dos o más variables. Si una de las variables cambia, la otra variable también puede cambiar, y dicho cambio puede ser predecible.

rule A summary of a predictable relationship that tells how to find the value of a variable. A rule may be given in words or as an equation. For example, this rule relates time, rate, and distance: distance is equal to rate times time, or $d = rt$.

regla Un resumen de una relación predecible que indica cómo hallar el valor de una variable. Se trata de un patrón que, debido a su coherencia, puede escribirse, convertirse en una ecuación, representarse gráficamente o utilizarse para hacer una tabla. Por ejemplo, la siguiente regla relaciona tiempo, velocidad y distancia: la distancia es igual al producto de la velocidad y el tiempo, o sea $d = rt$.

scale A labeling scheme used on each of the axes on a coordinate grid.

escala Un esquema de rotulación empleado en los ejes de una cuadrícula de coordenadas.

table A list of values for two or more variables that shows the relationship between them. Tables often represent data made from observations, from experiments, or from a series of arithmetic operations. A table may show a pattern of change between two variables that can be used to predict values not in the table.

tabla Una lista de valores para dos o más variables que muestra la relación existente entre ellas. Frecuentemente, las tablas contienen datos provenientes de observaciones, experimentos o de una serie de operaciones aritméticas. Una tabla puede mostrar un patrón de variación existente entre dos variables, el cual puede utilizarse para predecir los valores de otras entradas de la tabla.

variable A quantity that can change. Letters are often used as symbols to represent variables in rules or equations that describe patterns.

variable Una cantidad que puede cambiar. Suelen usarse letras como símbolos para representar las variables de las reglas o ecuaciones que describen patrones.

English/Spanish Glossary   **85**

Notes _____

_____

_____

_____

X

***x*-axis** The number line that is horizontal on a coordinate grid.

eje de las *x* La línea numérica horizontal en una cuadrícula de coordenadas.

Y

***y*-axis** The number line that is vertical on a coordinate grid.

eje de las *y* La línea numérica vertical en una cuadrícula de coordenadas.

86 Variables and Patterns

Notes

_____

_____

_____

_____

Academic Vocabulary

The following terms are important to your understanding of the mathematics in this unit. Knowing and using these words will help you in thinking, reasoning, representing, communicating your ideas, and making connections across ideas. When these words make sense to you, the investigations and problems will make more sense as well.

C

compare To tell or show how two things are alike and different.
related terms: analyze, relate

Sample: **Two river rafting companies offer tours. The Rocky River Company charges $150 per group. Bailey's Rafting charges $37.50 per person. Compare these offers, and explain for which situations each offer is a better deal.**

Each choice would cost the same for 4 people since 4 × $37.50 = $150. If a group has less than 4 people, Bailey's is the better deal. If there are more than 4 people, Rocky River is the better deal.

I can also use a table to find a solution.

people	1	2	3	4	5
Rocky River	$150	$150	$150	$150	$150
Bailey's	$37.50	$75	$112.50	$150	$187.50

The cost is the same for 4 people.

comparar Decir o mostrar en qué se parecen o en qué se diferencian dos cosas.
términos relacionados: analizar, relacionar

Ejemplo: **Dos compañías de navegación por rápidos ofrecen excursiones. La compañía Rocky River cobra $150 por grupo. Bailey's Rafting cobra $37.50 por persona. Compara estas ofertas y explica en qué situaciones cada una es la mejor opción.**

Cada opción costaría lo mismo por 4 personas, ya que 4 × $37.50 = $150. Si el grupo tuviera menos de 4 personas, Bailey's es la mejor opción. Si hay más de 4 personas, Rocky River es la mejor opción. También puedo usar una tabla para encontrar la solución.

personas	1	2	3	4	5
Rocky River	$150	$150	$150	$150	$150
Bailey's	$37.50	$75	$112.50	$150	$187.50

El costo es el mismo por 4 personas.

D

describe To explain or tell in detail. A written description can contain facts and other information needed to communicate your answer. A diagram or a graph may also be included.
related terms: express, explain, illustrate

Sample: **Describe the relationship between the number of photos and the price.**

Number of Photos	10	15	20	25
Price	$5.00	$7.50	$10.00	$12.50

For each increase of 5 photos, the price increases $2.50. If I divide 2.50 by 5, that's an increase of $0.50 for each photo.

describir Explicar o decir con detalles. Una descripción escrita puede tener datos y otra información necesaria para comunicar tu respuesta. También puedes incluir un diagrama o una gráfica.
términos relacionados: expresar, explicar, ilustrar

Ejemplo: **Describe la relación entre el número de fotos y el precio.**

Número de fotos	10	15	20	25
Pricio	$5.00	$7.50	$10.00	$12.50

Por cada 5 fotos, el precio aumenta $2.50. Si divido 2.50 por 5, resulta en un aumento de $0.50 por cada foto.

Academic Vocabulary **87**

Academic Vocabulary

Notes _____

_____

_____

_____

expect To use theoretical or experimental data to anticipate a certain outcome.

related terms: anticipate, predict

Sample: Cynthia counted her sit-ups. Based on her data, how many sit-ups would you expect her to do in 40 seconds? Would you expect this pattern to continue indefinitely?

Seconds	10	20	30
Number of Sit Ups	6	12	18

Cynthia's sit-ups increased by 6 every 10 seconds. Since 40 seconds is 10 more seconds than 30, I expect her to do 18 + 6 = 24 sit-ups.
I can also make a graph to represent this.

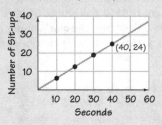

The graph shows 24 sit-ups at 40 seconds. I would not expect this pattern to continue because Cynthia will get tired and probably do less sit-ups.

esperar Usar datos teóricos o experimentales para anticipar cierto resultado.

términos relacionados: anticipar, predecir

Ejemplo: Cynthia contó sus abdominales. Según sus datos, ¿cuantos abdominales esperarías que ella hicera en 50 segundos? ¿Esperarías que este patrón continuara indefinidamente?

Segundos	10	20	30
N° de abdominales	6	12	18

Los abdominales de Cynthia aumentaron por 6 cada 10 segundos. Ya que 40 segundos son 10 segundos más que 30, espero que ella pueda hacer 18 + 6 = 24 abdominales. También puedo hacer una gráfica que represente estos datos.

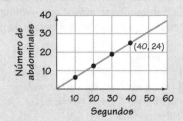

La gráfica muestra 24 abdominales en 40 segundos. No espero que este patrón continúe porque Cynthia se cansará y probablemente hará menos abdominales.

represent To stand for or take the place of something else. Symbols, equations, charts, and tables are often used to represent particular situations.

related terms: symbolize, stand for

Sample: Snowy Heights resort rents snowboards for $12 plus $3 for each hour. Write an equation to represent this situation. Explain what the variables and numbers in your equation represent.

My equation is $c = 12 + 3h$. The c represents the total cost. The 12 represents the initial charge for renting the snowboard. The h represents the number of hours rented and the 3 represents the hourly charge.

representar Reemplazar u ocupar el lugar de algo. Para representar situaciones particulares se suelen usar símbolos, ecuaciones, diagramas y tablas.

términos relacionados: simbolizar, significar

Ejemplo: El resort Snowy Heights alquila tablas para nieve a $12, más $3 por cada hora. Escribe una ecuación para representarlo. Explica lo que representan las variables y los números de tu ecuación.

Mi ecuación es $c = 12 + 3h$. La c representa el costo total. El 12 representa el cobro inicial por alquilar una tabla. La h representa el número de horas de alquila y el 3 representa el costo por hora.

88 Variables and Patterns

Notes _____

_____

_____

_____

Index

STUDENT PAGE

STUDENT PAGE

Index

Notes _____

_____

_____

_____

_____

90 Variables and Patterns

Notes

Acknowledgments

Team Credits

The people who made up the **Connected Mathematics 2** team—representing editorial, editorial services, design services, and production services—are listed below. Bold type denotes core team members.

Leora Adler, Judith Buice, Kerry Cashman, Patrick Culleton, Sheila DeFazio, Katie Hallahan, Richard Heater, **Barbara Hollingdale, Jayne Holman,** Karen Holtzman, **Etta Jacobs,** Christine Lee, Carolyn Lock, Catherine Maglio, **Dotti Marshall,** Rich McMahon, Eve Melnechuk, Kristin Mingrone, Terri Mitchell, **Marsha Novak,** Irene Rubin, Donna Russo, Robin Samper, Siri Schwartzman, **Nancy Smith,** Emily Soltanoff, **Mark Tricca,** Paula Vergith, Roberta Warshaw, Helen Young

Additional Credits

Diana Bonfilio, Mairead Reddin, Michael Torocsik, nSight, Inc.

Technical Illustration

WestWords, Inc.

Cover Design

tom white.images

Photo

2 t, David Maenza/SuperStock; **2 b,** SuperStock/PictureQuest; **3,** Peter Griffith/Masterfile; **5,** Michael Kevin Daly/Corbis; **7,** RubberBall Productions/Index Stock Imagery, Inc.; **12,** Medford Taylor/SuperStock; **13,** Marcio Jose/AP/Wide World Photos; **17,** Michael Newman/PhotoEdit; **18,** Roy Ooms/Masterfile; **25,** Big Cheese Photo/SuperStock; **26 l,** David Maenza/SuperStock; **26 r,** Free Agents Limited/Corbis; **28,** Tom Stewart/Corbis; **30,** Brian Bailey/Getty Images, Inc.; **32,** Kindra Clineff/Index Stock Imagery, Inc.; **34,** Chris Trotman/Corbis; **35,** Michael Kooren/Corbis; **41,** Wilson Goodrich/Index Stock Imagery, Inc.; **43,** Chris Cole/Corbis; **46,** Paul Barton/Corbis; **49,** Jeff Greenberg/AGE Fotostock; **55,** BERNSTEIN KEITH-FSP/GAMMA; **59,** Rob Walls/Alamy; **64,** Michael Newman/PhotoEdit; **66,** SuperStock/PictureQuest; **75,** Kevin Fleming/Corbis; **79,** Bill Bachman/Photo Researchers, Inc.

Data Sources

Tiger cub data on page 35 from "Typical Weights for Tiger Cubs" used with permission of the Tiger Missing Link Foundation www.tigerlink.org.

Lewes Ferry Fares on page 75 adapted from www.capemaylewesferry.com.

Note: Every effort has been made to locate the copyright owner of the material reprinted in this book. Omissions brought to our attention will be corrected in subsequent editions.

Notes _____

_____

_____

_____

Centimeter Grid Paper

PACING: _____

Mathematical Goals

_____
_____
_____
_____

Launch

_____
_____
_____
_____
_____
_____
_____
_____

Materials

Explore

_____
_____
_____
_____
_____
_____
_____
_____

Materials

Summarize

_____
_____
_____
_____
_____
_____
_____
_____

Materials

Glossary

C

change To become different. For example, temperatures rise and fall, prices increase and decrease, and so on. In mathematics, quantities that change are called *variables*.

coordinate graph A graphical representation of pairs of related numerical values that shows the relationship between two variables. It relates the independent variable (shown on the *x*-axis) and the dependent variable (shown on the *y*-axis).

coordinate pair An ordered pair of numbers used to locate a point on a coordinate grid. The first number in a coordinate pair is the value for the *x*-coordinate, and the second number is the value for the *y*-coordinate.

D

dependent variable One of the two variables in a relationship. Its value depends upon or is determined by the other variable called the *independent variable*. For example, the cost of a long-distance phone call (dependent variable) depends on how long you talk (independent variable).

E

equation, formula A rule containing variables that represents a mathematical relationship. An example is the formula for finding the area of a circle: $A = \pi r^2$.

I

independent variable One of the two variables in a relationship. Its value determines the value of the other variable called the *dependent variable*. If you organize a bike tour, for example, the number of people who register to go (independent variable) determines the cost for renting bikes (dependent variable).

P

pattern A change that occurs in a predictable way. For example, the squares on a checkerboard form a pattern in which the colors of the squares alternate between red and black. The sequence of square numbers: 1, 4, 9, 16, ... forms a pattern in which the numbers increase by the next odd number. That is, 4 is 3 more than 1, 9 is 5 more than 4, 16 is 7 more than 9, and so on.

R

relationship An association between two or more variables. If one of the variables changes, the other variable may also change, and the change may be predictable.

rule A summary of a predictable relationship that tells how to find the value of a variable. A rule may be given in words or as an equation. For example, this rule relates time, rate, and distance: distance is equal to rate times time, or $d = rt$.

S

scale A labeling scheme used on each of the axes on a coordinate grid.

T

table A list of values for two or more variables that shows the relationship between them. Tables often represent data made from observations, from experiments, or from a series of arithmetic operations. A table may show a pattern of change between two variables that can be used to predict values for other entries in the table.

V

variable A quantity that can change. Letters are often used as symbols to represent variables in rules or equations that describe patterns.

X

x-axis The number line that is horizontal on a coordinate grid.

Y

y-axis The number line that is vertical on a coordinate grid.

Index

Acknowledgments

Team Credits

The people who made up the **Connected Mathematics 2** team—representing editorial, editorial services, design services, and production services—are listed below. Bold type denotes core team members.

Leora Adler, Judith Buice, Kerry Cashman, Patrick Culleton, Sheila DeFazio, Richard Heater, **Barbara Hollingdale, Jayne Holman,** Karen Holtzman, **Etta Jacobs,** Christine Lee, Carolyn Lock, Catherine Maglio, **Dotti Marshall,** Rich McMahon, Eve Melnechuk, Kristin Mingrone, Terri Mitchell, **Marsha Novak,** Irene Rubin, Donna Russo, Robin Samper, Siri Schwartzman, **Nancy Smith,** Emily Soltanoff, **Mark Tricca,** Paula Vergith, Roberta Warshaw, Helen Young

Additional Credits

Diana Bonfilio, Mairead Reddin, Michael Torocsik, nSight, Inc.

Technical Illustration

Schawk, Inc.

Cover Design

tom white.images